THATCH

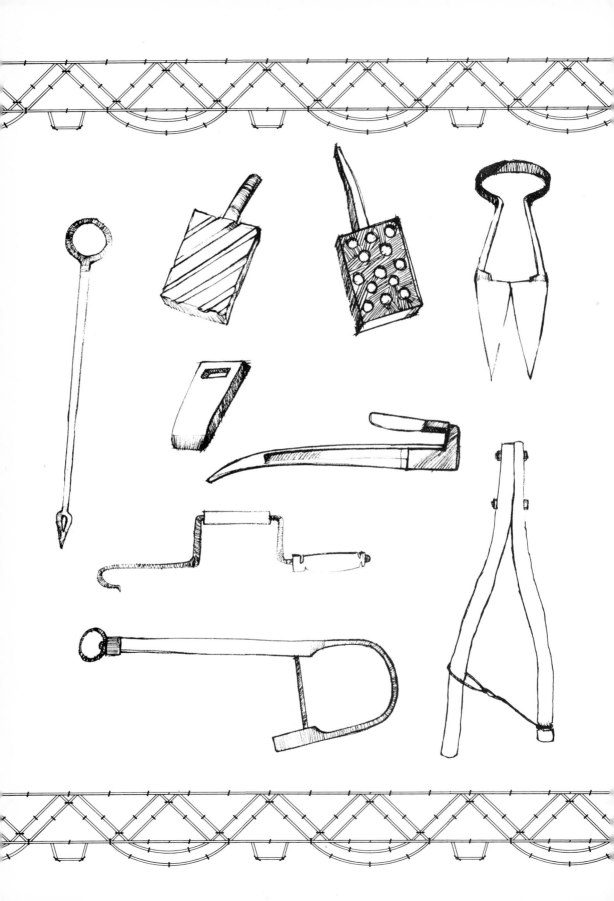

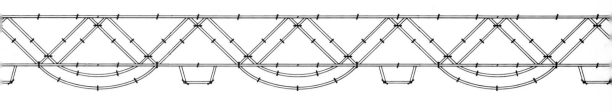

T·H·A·T·C·H

Robert C. West

DAVID & CHARLES
Newton Abbot London
THE MAIN STREET PRESS
Pittstown, New Jersey

British Library Cataloguing in Publication Data

West, Robert C.
   Thatch; a manual for owners, surveyors,
   architects and builders.
   1. Thatched roofs——England   2. Roofing
   ——England
   I. Title
   695   TH2435

   ISBN 0–7153–8849–5

© Robert C. West 1987

Typeset by ABM Typographics Limited, Hull
and printed in Great Britain
by Redwood Burn Limited, Trowbridge, Wilts
for David & Charles Publishers plc
Brunel House   Newton Abbot   Devon   England

First American edition 1988

Published by
The Main Street Press, Inc.
William Case House
Pittstown, New Jersey 08867

Library of Congress Cataloging-in-Publication Data
West, Robert (Robert C.)
   Thatch: a complete guide to the ancient craft of
thatching.

   Bibliography: p.
   Includes index.
   1. Thatched roofs.   I. Title
TH2435.W47 1988   695   87–15377
ISBN 1–55562–044–2

Contents

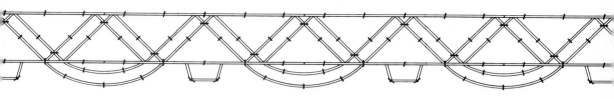

Introduction

Few people fail to recognise the aesthetic qualities of a thatched roof and those fortunate enough to live under one will appreciate it in terms of comfort, but the general mystique which surrounds thatch means that it is little understood as a practical roofing material.

The subject is so wide and varied, with so many regional and national differences, and so many exceptions to the rules, that full detailed coverage is beyond the scope of this book, which is not intended to be the definitive work. Nor will the following chapters teach you how to thatch — the craft can be learnt only by experience — but it is hoped that they will explain most that the owner, architect, builder and estate agent may need to know about design, materials and techniques, and provide advice on ways of prolonging the useful life of a thatch while avoiding the most common pitfalls.

Thatch has both advantages and disadvantages which must be taken into account. However, there can be no doubt that its insulative properties compare very favourably with those of other roofing materials. Recent tests carried out to establish the thermal conductance (U) values of thatch illustrate how reasonable is the time-honoured claim of the thatchowner that his prized cottage is 'warm in winter and cool in summer'.

A U-value is a figure, determined by experiment, indicating the rate at which heat energy passes through a certain wall, roof or floor structure. The figure itself is derived from the number of watts of heat energy which will pass through 1sq m of the material for every 1°C temperature difference between one side and the other. The lower the figure the more efficient the insulative properties.

Present building regulations require a 'normal' roof, ie tiled, to have a minimum U-value of 0.35 watts/sq m/°C and it is necessary to have 100mm (4in) of fibreglass insulation between the joists to achieve this figure. A water reed thatched roof, 300mm (12in) thick at a pitch angle of 45 degrees has a U-value of 0.35. This is because the structure of the thatch is cellular and in addition the direction of the movement of warm convected air is always back into the loft cavity. New proposals for insulation standards demanding a U-value of 0.35 will require the use of 100mm (4in) of fibreglass in a conventional roof, whereas thatch can already meet

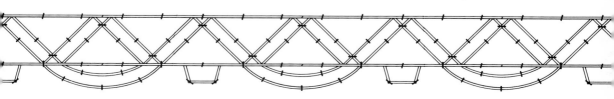

Plate 1 A beautiful example of the thatcher's craft, on a house in Devon

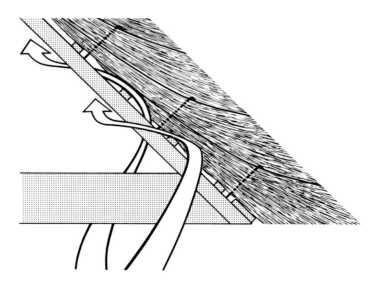

Fig 1 Thatch, being cellular, is an excellent insulator — but in addition, the direction of each piece of thatch guides convected air back into the roof space

these modern requirements (though its U-value will vary according to thickness, density, pitch, etc).

The sound insulative qualities of thatch are also surprisingly high. During production of a film on thatching for children's television some years ago, it was noted that as little as one inch of thatch between the hidden microphone and the speaker would halt recording.

Construction costs are lower for thatch when compared with conventional roofing in that there are no gutters, downpipes, soakaways, soffit board or the attendant painting and decorating. And from a conservation point of view thatch is less demanding on the land as the raw materials do not require quarrying or mining. Water reed, which is widely used in many areas, is a natural annual crop that, properly maintained, promotes the survival of wildlife and improves the environment generally; perhaps even more importantly, it grows in areas which are otherwise agriculturally unviable. The alternative thatching material, straw, is a by-product of an essential food harvest. So neither product creates wastage or is a drain on the world's natural resources.

There are only two major disadvantages to owning a thatched roof. First, because thatch is fairly combustible it incurs higher insurance premiums than slate or tiles; second, the process of thatching is more labour intensive than other methods of roofing and this will be reflected in costs, though these will not be disproportionately high in comparison with other quality roofing materials.

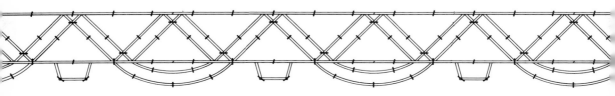

1
Thatch — Past, Present and Future

Thatching is one of the oldest crafts in the building industry still practised today. A brief outline of its history will explain how it developed and why it went through an unpopular period.

The use of vegetable matter as a roof covering dates back thousands of years. Clods of earth were placed on wattle huts by the earliest tribes. Excavations at Corinth in Greece show that temples built around 750BC were thatched with straw; and in Britain, archaeologists have found evidence of buildings with straw roof coverings dating back to 500BC. Apart from being almost the only, and therefore the cheapest, form of roofing material, thatch was also the lightest. This was very important on houses built with walls that could not support heavy loads, such as the cob cottages once very common in Devon, which were constructed from a mixture of clay and straw. Early humble cottages built from timber and daub (a mixture of plaster and whitewash) were thatched, generally with straw though reed and heather were quite common; where these were not available any other suitable materials such as broom or bracken were used. In those days people built houses for their own occupation and even though they were amateurs, and their methods were unsophisticated, their thatches were constructed with a considerable degree of skill.

In the Highlands and islands of Scotland, thatch was, over the centuries, the traditional roof covering for crofts and farmhouses. Not only did its availability and flexibility in handling allow it to be used anywhere but its lightness avoided the need for heavy roof trusses and rafters. This was a vital factor in a location that suffered from a scarcity of timber, especially in the outlying islands where the weather conditions made tree growing virtually impossible. Therefore wood was very valuable and had to be imported by boat or collected from the seashore by beachcombing.

In the Middle Ages thatch was sometimes used as a form of temporary roof covering on buildings during the course of construction, but then because of its effectiveness was left permanently in position. Similarly, thatch was used as temporary protection for the tops of walls under construction to prevent frost damage. Even today, in and around Wilt-

shire, Berkshire and Hampshire, walls are still found with a capping or weathering of straw thatch as a shield against the elements.

During early Norman times, when other roofing materials such as clay tiles, started to appear, thatch still retained its popularity. Not only was it a cheaper covering but because of its lightness it could be supported by a roof frame that was light and simple in design and therefore also comparatively inexpensive. In buildings around this time rough wood, often with the bark intact, was used for rafters and laths. Builders simply took advantage of the most readily available material, sometimes even old ships' timbers, and very rarely was an attempt made to get rid of irregularities. The roofs were constructed so that the thatch projected over the house walls, thereby producing wide eaves so that water was thrown well clear of the walls which were often porous. This feature gave birth to that well-known character the 'eavesdropper', a person who crept under the overhanging edge of the roof to listen clandestinely to what was being said within the house.

Unfortunately the popularity of thatch was to be a factor contributing to its demise. Thatched houses built in close proximity helped to account for the frequent and disastrous fires that swept through the narrow streets of medieval cities. London was devastated in 1077, 1087 and 1161; also in 1161, Canterbury, Exeter and Winchester were destroyed. In 1180 Winchester was again almost burnt to the ground, followed by Glastonbury in 1184, Chichester in 1187 and Worcester in 1202. It is not really surprising that the authorities decided that something had to be done, and this led to the Ordinance of 1212, arguably the first building regulation in force in London. This prohibited any future covering of roofs with thatch of any kind; also all existing thatched roofs had to be coated with a whitewash plaster daub. Failure to comply with the regulations meant the building would be demolished. However, like most medieval laws, this one was widely abused and ignored and, as history shows, thatch was still prevalent in London fifty years later.

In 1264 Simon de Montfort, in his efforts to overthrow the throne, planned to make use of the combustibility of thatch as a means of furthering his own ends, probably an event unique in history. Hundreds of chickens with flaming brands tied to their feet were to be set loose in London, setting light to the thatched roofs and burning the city down while de Montfort seized power in the confusion. Whether or not it rained that night is not recorded, but the plan did not succeed.

The Ordinance of 1212 was eventually to be introduced in towns throughout England. However, its powers were slow to take effect; in Norwich, tiling of roofs was not compulsory until 1509. In Wales, the

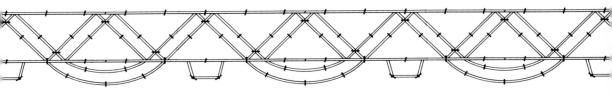

custom (by then the law was obsolete) of whitewashing thatch in order to make it burn less easily continued until the early twentieth century.

At the same time as restrictions on thatch building were formulated in the thirteenth century, tile making started to spread throughout the counties of south and east England. As thatched roofs needed renovating they were very often (in towns, without exception) replaced by tiles. This often accounts for the apparent bareness of many medieval buildings as they appear today, where thatch has been replaced by a sparser covering of slates or tiles. The signs to look for are a roof with a pitch of 50 to 60 degrees and chimneys that seem very high in relation to the rest of the building (necessary with a thatched roof to lessen the risk of fire starting from a piece of flaming ash or cinder). Throughout the Middle Ages, tile making flourished, especially where a location that was well served for water transport also happened to have good local supplies of light clay, such as was the case with Woolwich in south-east London.

Another factor which contributed to the demise of thatching was that those who chose to take up the profession did not receive very great rewards. The accounts of a seventeenth century landowner have this to say about thatchers:

> They had a large appetite — paid 6d [2½p]/day plus food in summer and 4d [1½p]/day plus food in winter. Breakfast at 8 Dinner at 12 Supper at 7, each meal consisted of 4 courses. If they provided their own food they got an extra 4d [1½p]/day.

Apart from the growth of the tile-making industry, the production of Welsh slate began on a massive scale in 1820 and the ease of rail transport soon made these two forms of roofing freely available in places where thatch was already established. Also, the French wars had raised the price of wheat and straw to a prohibitive level, so not only was thatch being ousted by the fashion for newer, permanent materials, but in many parts of the country it had ceased to be the cheapest and most easily obtainable roof covering. In addition it was often thought to be too humble and inferior for use on important buildings, as was the case with Reydon church near Southwold in East Suffolk: in 1880 the church was tiled on the side of the roof that faced the road and thatched on the other side which was out of sight of passers-by. In contrast, oddly enough, thatch was at this time being adopted by the wealthy as a picturesque adornment and appeared in many country estates.

It is true to say that in the first half of this century there was a further decline in thatching due to a number of reasons, not least of all the two world wars. There was a decline in the number of thatchers, cheaper roofing materials became available, insurance premiums rose and generally it was seen as an unfashionable, dying craft. However, since the early 1970s the industry has gone through a renaissance and far from being a dying craft it is potentially a growth industry.

12

Plate 2 With only eight days allowed for the entire roof to be covered in water reed, the first thatched house in the Ideal Home Exhibition takes shape

Water reed of excellent quality is available at any time of the year and supplies of winter wheat straw are improving, although there will always be the occasional bad harvest. Most varieties of winter wheat suitable for thatching are reasonably high yielding in cereal content, so provided farmers are compensated adequately for the additional problems they take on when supplying roofing straw they will produce enough for the thatchers' needs. Market forces will dictate the availability of combed wheat reed and long straw; the machinery to produce these materials is available and new equipment has recently been built. (See Chapter 2 for an account of thatching materials and their production.)

Similarly, there is a ready market for thatched roofs, provided prices are kept to a reasonable level. For the past 10 years nearly half the thatching work in the United Kingdom has been on 'newbuild' thatch, either for brand-new architect-designed homes or extensions to existing cottages, and the cost could drop dramatically if simpler building designs were used. Chapter 6 gives details of methods of roof construction that will not only allow thatching to be carried out with maximum speed and efficiency but will ensure that the material has the best chance of achieving a reasonable life-span. There is still tremendous scope within design for innovations that will substantially improve the general future of thatch.

The attention of both the public and the building industry has been aroused since the thatching of the House of the Year at the Ideal Home Exhibition in 1984 and the development of thatched properties by Bovis

13

PERSPECTIVA: SR. JORGE L. BENITEZ ARREDONDO

Fig 2

SOLAR Nº 18 — MANZANA Nº 84

Fig 3

PINARES DE MALDONAD·

Fig 4

Plate 3 On completion, the 'Finchampstead', named House of the Year 1984, excited interest throughout the building industry both in the United Kingdom and abroad

at Woolstones, Milton Keynes, the following year. There is every reason to expect other major developers of residential property to look closely at the advantages. Despite the four thatched houses at Woolstones being considerably more expensive than other houses on the estate, which had similar specifications, they attracted greater interest than their tiled counterparts.

There is also a growing enthusiasm for thatch in Europe and there are some wonderful designs coming out of the United States of America. The latter definitely have the touch of Walt Disney fantasy-land, but are exciting examples of what can be done with traditional materials and revolutionary ideas (see pages 14–19).

Another area of potential regrowth might be found in the large number of rural properties which were once thatched and are now roofed with anything from corrugated iron to slates, some still with the original thatch intact beneath. At the time of roof change the probable reason was cost; however, the drop in capital value of the property must surely outweigh the short-term saving, and how much more attractive such houses would be with their original charm reinstated. The thatcher has the great good fortune to be able to put flair and art into his work and so leave something more beautiful than most other builders; but it is for the thatching industry to further its own interests if the craft is to survive in the modern world.

2
Thatching Materials

The main thatching materials in common usage in the United Kingdom are water reed (*Phragmites australis*) and wheat straw. Correctly laid and firmly fixed, *Phragmites* makes the most durable thatch; a particularly fine type is Norfolk reed.

In general terms there are two varieties of wheat — spring and winter — the latter being most suitable for thatching when, according to the treatment it receives after reaping and binding, it is used in the form of combed wheat reed (often known as Devon reed) or long straw. Spring wheat is occasionally prepared for thatching purposes, though it makes a poor substitute.

Other cereal straws have been employed for roofing over the years — rye and, in Ireland, oat straw thatches are still sometimes seen — and heather (ling) thatch, though rare, can be found in some parts of the country. Sedge (*Cladium mariscus*), which combines well with water reed, is often used for ridging.

(For a comparison of life-spans of thatching materials and a guide to their identification *in situ* see Chapter 3.)

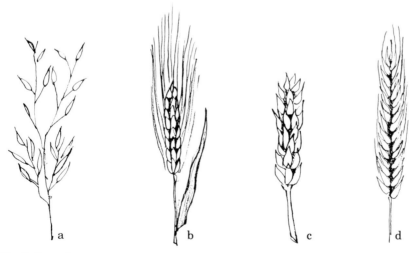

Fig 5 Cereal straws sometimes employed as thatching materials: a) oats, b) barley, c) wheat, d) rye

WATER REED

Water reed is an abundant plant occurring in wet places throughout the temperate parts of the world and whose aerial shoots form reeds. In Britain it is most common in lowland and coastal marshes, but it is also widespread throughout the country in ditches and ponds. The largest and best quality beds are in East Anglia, in the wetlands near the main Waveney, Bure and Little Ouse rivers and their tributaries, and the Broads. There are also a few large reed-growing areas in south Wales, on the south coast of England and in north-east Scotland.

Water reed is used almost exclusively for thatching in Europe and grows in vast quantities from Poland, Rumania and Hungary to Austria, France and Holland. Although it may vary in length, texture and colour, it has similar physical qualities no matter where it originates. Thatching reed from the Continent tends to be coarser and longer than Norfolk reed, which itself can vary a great deal depending upon whether the reed beds

*Plate 4 Water reed
(Phragmites australis)*

are fresh or salt water, whether the reed is cut from the centre of the bed or whether winter and spring are wet or dry. Most thatchers would prefer Norfolk reed, if available, but every year there is a shortfall and reed must be imported from other parts of Europe. The thatched property owner need have no qualms as the material, although more difficult to lay, will last just as long as Norfolk reed and perhaps longer.

In the past, reeds were exploited wherever they grew, but due to increased overheads for harvesting, storage and so on only the larger areas are now used. Most reed beds were originally laid out for manual harvesting with boats being used to transport the crop. Dykes across the larger reed beds tended to be parallel and at right angles to the main river, making the bed rectangular. These ditches were used to control the water levels.

Under suitable management, marshes can be encouraged to produce practically pure stands of reed crops apparently indefinitely, with no loss of quality or quantity and only slight variations caused by the effect of seasonal conditions on growth. Neglected marshes, on the other hand, will steadily deteriorate and become clogged with weeds, alders, willows and even birch. The three main factors in reed management are: water control, weed control and harvesting routine.

Water control

As the best thatching reeds are grown in water, the beds should remain flooded for most of the year. This water should be moving as reed will not thrive in completely stagnant conditions. In some instances, such as when the beds are part of the general Broads system or large water courses, there can be no control. When control is practicable, its main purpose is to maintain a high level during the winter to prevent the running off of water during a dry spring. If a pumping station, as opposed to sluices, is available then it can be used to drain the beds to facilitate the use of machinery during harvesting.

A high water level during the early spring will protect the young colts (new growth) from frost; this is particularly necessary if the reed is of high quality. However, should the colts of coarse reed be killed by frost, it is thought that two to three new shoots of finer growth will be produced.

Weed control

Weed control is best maintained by high water levels, as a dry bed will soon become colonised by grasses, brambles and nettles, and other unwanted growth. This is not always possible over the whole marsh or bed, and areas will slowly begin to contain a higher proportion of mixed marsh vegetation. There will also be marginal areas where the reed is not yet dominant enough to be worth cutting. In such cases, a burn and flood

Fig 6 Phragmites

23

practice is usual, where the old vegetation, during February and March (when it is at its driest), is set alight. The new shoots will not yet be numerous enough to take much harm and the fire will make a clean sweep of any dead vegetation and allow the fast-growing reed a chance to get away ahead of the weeds. The water level is then increased and maintained throughout the summer.

Harvest
The traditional time for cutting reed is when the 'flag' is down and the leaf has fallen from the stem, usually after mid December. This can continue until the first colts appear towards the end of April/beginning of May. To cut later than this will damage the colts and possibly reduce the amount of reed produced the following year.

Reed can be cut annually (single wale) or every other year (double wale), the latter being most usual. Although, for thatching, a single wale is better, as it contains very few dead reeds, it is less profitable for the marsh men as it is a thinner crop and therefore more effort is needed to obtain the required number of bundles. A reed bed of high productivity should produce around 400 bundles per 0.4ha (1 acre) single wale or 400 to 500 bundles double wale.

Methods of harvesting vary from hand-cutting with a scythe to mechanical operations using a rice cutter, allen scythes or a sieger, an amphibious vehicle that both cuts and binds. After cutting, the reed bundles are opened, cleaned of leaves and debris, rebundled and stacked to dry out on the marshes. When dry, they can then be transported either into storage or direct to the thatcher.

The specification given below is for the highest quality reed:

Diameter of stem:	minimum 2mm (1/12in); maximum 6mm (1/4in); optimum on average 3–4mm (1/10–1/6in) at cut base.
Height:	minimum 0.9m (35in); maximum 1.8m (6ft); optimum 1.37–1.53m (54–60in).
Circumference of bundle:	measured 30cm (12in) above cut to base — 55cm (22in); measured 30cm (12in) below flowering heads — 15–20cm (6–8in).
Circumference of one fathom (six bundles):	measured 30cm (12in) from base — 1.8m (6ft).

Bundles should contain 99 per cent pure *Phragmites* with minimal dead leaf and should be bright in colour. In any consignment of reed 60 per cent of the bundles should be 1.2–1.5m (48–60in) in height; 20 per cent 1.5–1.8m (60–70in); and 20 per cent 0.9–1.2m (35–48in).

Plate 5 Phragmites *carries a flower-head resembling a soft, feathery plume*

Plate 6 Norfolk reed being cut by hand — a cold, laborious task. In many areas mechanical scythes and binders have revolutionised the harvesting process

Plate 7 After cutting and binding the reed is loaded aboard a barge to be taken back to dry land

Plate 8 Each bundle is opened and cleaned of
debris before being retied to await delivery to
the thatcher

Plate 9 Water reed may vary considerably in
length

SEDGE

Commonly used as a ridging material, sedge grows in the same areas as reed and is usually maintained as a complementary crop. Each species will infiltrate the other's land. Sedge is an evergreen, continuously growing plant (with triangular, serrated leaves) which can be cut at any time of the year, but for practical reasons the crop is better taken during the summer, work traditionally starting in late July. This splits the harvest between reed and sedge but also tends to kill any reed that may be growing in amongst the sedge. Also, summer cutting ensures adequate growth before the onset of winter.

Sedge, unlike reed, is harvested every four years which produces long growth most suitable for ridging material. If it is cut more often, the sedge will not be long enough for the thatcher and other marsh plants will be encouraged to grow, thereby reducing the crop. It is cut either by hand or with an allen scythe and though not usually cleaned to the extent of reed, the worst debris is taken out.

The same type of management policy as for reed is used, apart from the timing of water height. Where water reed beds are flooded during the summer months, the sedge bed is drained during this period to facilitate harvest. Burning, when necessary, is carried out from June to August to

Plate 10 Sedge (Cladium mariscus) *flourishes in the same marshy habitat as water reed and is usually grown as a complementary crop. It is used for ridging and blends well with reed*

maximise the effect on reeds and other marsh plants. This has no permanent effect on the sedge which quickly starts regrowing.

Because the management of reed and sedge marshes is basically organic (there is limited use of chemicals or fertilisers) an abundance of natural flora and fauna is being preserved in these areas. The swallowtail butterfly is now seen in numbers only in the Broads areas of Norfolk, where the sedge beds usually contain the milk parsley on which its larvae feed. Reed beds also contain many rare species of birds — bitterns, bearded tits and marsh harriers for example.

COMBED WHEAT REED

Although now used widely throughout England, combed wheat reed is essentially a Westcountry material, which is why it is frequently called Devon reed. It is normally one of the accepted varieties of winter wheat (see below) which after having been cut and stooked at harvest is put through a threshing machine which also 'combs' the stems. The process prepares the material so that it can be used for thatching in a similar manner to water reed, with a similar surface texture in that only the butts are visible on the surface of the coat.

Varieties
The older the variety of wheat it would seem the more popular it is with the thatcher. The traditional Little Joss, Elite and Square-headed Masters are still occasionally grown, but as modern farming dictates that a reasonable yield of grain is achieved, more recent varieties are being used, Maris Widgeon and Maris Huntsman being the most common. Aquila has also been found to be of use to the thatcher. Grain yields range from a little over 3 tonnes/Ha (1.2 tons per acre) for the older varieties, to a more respectable 5 tonnes/Ha (2 tons per acre) for Maris Widgeon and slightly more again for Huntsman and Aquila. Conversely, straw yields are higher for the old varieties.

Cultivation
Winter wheat is sown at the end of September or in early October with a low nitrogen seed bed fertiliser. The largest single factor in thatching-straw husbandry is the need to keep nitrogen levels low, that is less than 100kg per hectare (89¼lb per acre). This is to prevent a high level of nitrogen being retained in the straw and possibly reducing its longevity when on the roof by creating an environment for greater microbiological

Plate 11 Winter wheat is cut and tied by a binder in one operation
Plate 12 The sheaves are picked up and stooked in the field to ripen

activity (see page 42). Winter wheat should receive as a seed-bed dressing 25kg per hectare (22¼lb per acre) of nitrogen, 50kg per hectare (44½lb per acre) of potash and 50kg per hectare (44½lb per acre) of phosphates, whilst the spring top-dressing of straight nitrogen will be in the region of 50–75kg per hectare (44½–67lb per acre). These ratios may vary according to the soil or particular climatic conditions.

A normal regime of good husbandry using chemical sprays to keep the crop clean of weeds and disease free has been used in the past, and will continue as long as there are no contra-indications. Weeds reduce yields of corn and straw, act as hosts to pests and diseases, and generally hinder the harvesting and processing of the crop. Eyespot fungus will seriously weaken the stem of the plant and make it more prone to 'lodging' (being blown down flat). Fortunately, Maris Widgeon, one of the better varieties for thatching straw, has a good level of resistance to this disease. A two-year break in the cereal cycle will help clear the ground of the infection. Mildew and rusts will affect the quality of the straw, and its longevity when on the roof will be reduced.

Plate 13 A rick of winter wheat awaiting combing and threshing. It has a thin layer of thatch to protect it from rain

Plate 14 The comber and thresher is moved into the field and fed directly from the rick. Note the straw bond which holds the thatch

Harvesting and processing

By the time the straw is harvested the crop should ideally be in the region of 1.2m (4 feet) tall and have straight stems. The straw should be yellow with the grain still slightly cheesy in texture, whilst the nodes should still show a slight greenness. After cutting and binding, the sheaves should be stooked in the field to ripen for five to fourteen days depending on the weather conditions. Then, until combing and threshing can begin, the sheaves should be removed to either an outside rick, thatched or tarpaulined over, or put in a barn — possibly for some months. Problems that can arise during this period are rooks attacking the sheaves, and rats getting into the stack or rick. However, ricking or storing the crop are not universal practices and some straw is produced 'from the field' in good harvesting conditions.

Before the wheat enters the thresher the sheaves are passed through a comber — a fairly complicated piece of equipment which holds the straw butts captive in a pair of belts while a drum with iron teeth rotates and 'combs' the wheat, removing any weeds and rubbish and much of the leaf. Once the grain has been extracted the combed wheat reed is trussed into bundles with the butts at one end and the ears at the other.

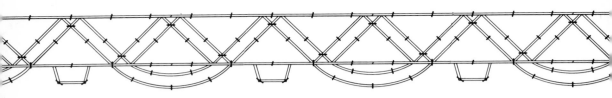

LONG STRAW

Long straw is used widely throughout the United Kingdom, although predominantly in the central and southern and south eastern regions. It is normally winter wheat, grown and harvested in exactly the same manner as that used for producing combed wheat reed; only the processing after reaping and binding differs. The straw is not combed but is fed directly into a threshing drum with concave-shaped beaters; during the operation the stems are frequently broken, and ears and butts become mixed. Not only is the leaf retained but also a quantity of whatever else happened to be growing in the field at the time of harvesting.

The straw is no longer than combed wheat reed but is fixed on to the roof with a greater length of stem exposed to the weather.

HEATHER (LING)

Heather is becoming less widely used although occasionally examples of it can still be seen, especially in parts of Kent and Surrey and on crofters' cottages in Scotland, Wales and Ireland. The material is coarse, tangled, dark in colour and of twiglike appearance, readily distinguishable from reed or straw. Although reasonably flexible when cut, it quickly becomes brittle.

For information on hazel and willow production, refer to the Further Reading list on page 155.

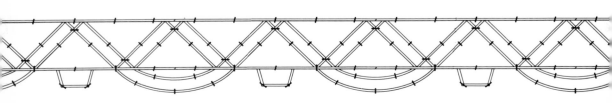

3
Identifying Thatch

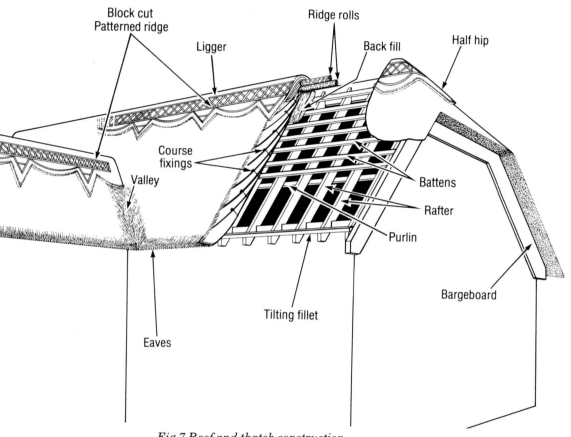

Block cut
Patterned ridge

Ridge rolls

Ligger

Back fill

Half hip

Course
fixings

Battens

Valley

Rafter

Purlin

Bargeboard

Tilting fillet

Eaves

Fig 7 Roof and thatch construction

Perhaps one of the most important yet most difficult things to learn about thatch, and its infinite variations of style, quality and age, is correct identification of the type of material with which a roof is covered. Even from a distance a thatched roof will have many telltale signs and all these must be noted so that a 'checklist' can be compiled. The task will be made easier if a pair of binoculars are to hand. To start with, the following points must be considered.

Plate 15 A fine example of combed wheat reed thatch on top of centuries of long straw, showing the typical rounded line

Is the roof rounded, soft and curvate, or is it flat, angular and more accurately following the shape of the roofing timbers?

Because of the method of fixing, and to some extent the nature of the materials, both long straw and combed wheat reed tend to have rounded, 'soft' looking lines (see Plate 15). These are accentuated by layer upon layer of thatch having been added over a period of centuries ending up with a total thickness often several feet deep. Water reed, on the other hand, is traditionally laid on bare timber with all old thatch first being removed and therefore more precisely follows the line of the timbers, showing flat surfaces and angular hips and valleys (see Plate 16).

Plate 16 Water reed is usually laid on to bare timber and follows the angles of the roof

Is there wire mesh over the whole roof, on the ridge only, or none at all?

It is unusual for water reed, particularly in the first half of its life, to have wire mesh on the coat, though it will frequently be wired on the ridge only (see Plate 17). Combed wheat reed in the west of England is rarely covered with wire, though this is not the case in the remainder of the country, and long straw nearly always has protective netting (see Plate 18).

Plate 17 Normally only the ridge of a water reed thatch is covered with wire mesh

Plate 18 A full covering of wire netting protects long straw and combed wheat reed from damage by birds or rodents

35

Is the ridge 'block cut' and 'patterned' or 'flush'?
Water reed is normally finished with a block-cut ridge, decoratively patterned with spars (see Plate 19), whereas both long straw and combed wheat reed can be finished with either a block-cut or flush ridge (see Plate 20).

Plate 19 The finishing touches are made to a decorative block-cut ridge

Plate 20 Combed wheat reed with a flush ridge

Is there an exposed 'ligger' (a spar of hazel or willow) running along the line of the eaves, vertically up the gable, or around the hips?

Only long straw requires an exposed ligger, or cross-spar pattern at the eaves and along gables (see Plate 21), to hold it in position. Thus any thatch without this addition is normally one of the other two materials. But beware the exceptions. Maybe the owner demanded a ligger or possibly the roof was extended in combed wheat reed and a pattern was fixed to match the original long straw roof (see Plate 22).

Plate 21 Long straw, showing ligger work to the eaves and gables together with a flush ridge

Plate 22 Cross-spar patterning has been contrived on the eaves of a new combed wheat reed extension to match the original long straw roof

Thus already, from some considerable distance, one can begin to put the pieces together. Having arrived at the eaves line, other telltale signs can be ticked off the checklist.

Are there only butts visible on the surface of the coat, or can lengths of stems be seen — some butts down, some ears down?
If the surface of the coat exposes only the butts of the thatching material it is either water reed or combed wheat reed (see Plate 23). If it is of coarser texture with butts and ears showing it is long straw (see Plate 24).

Plate 23 Only the butts show on the surface of a combed wheat reed or water reed thatch

Plate 24 Long straw — stem lengths are exposed and ears and butts are mixed. Note the exposed hazel ligger at the eaves line

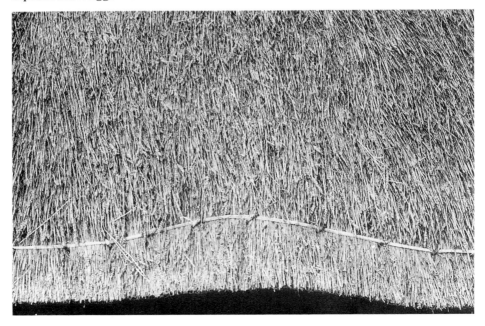

Has the eaves line been cut to shape, thus leaving the butts clearly cut at 45 degrees, or are the butts still cut at right angles to the stems showing that the thatch has been dressed or pushed into shape?
If the eaves and gables have been cut to shape it is usually either long straw or combed wheat reed (see Plate 25). Water reed, being so much stiffer and stronger, can be dressed, beaten or pushed to shape under the eaves and therefore the butt ends will still show the original square cut made when the reed was harvested (see Plate 26). Occasionally a thatcher will dress wheat reed eaves rather than cut them but this is not generally accepted practice.

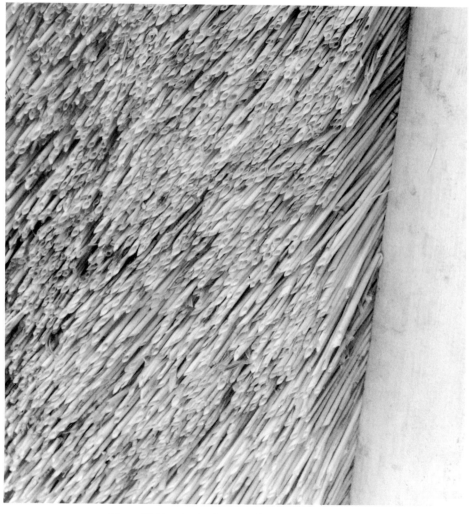

Plate 25 Combed wheat reed eaves cut to shape

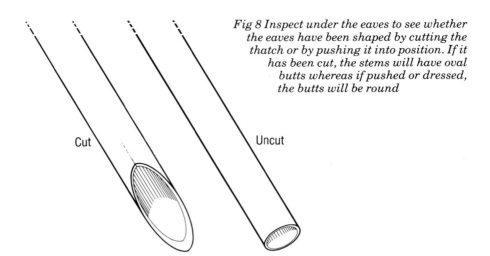

Fig 8 Inspect under the eaves to see whether the eaves have been shaped by cutting the thatch or by pushing it into position. If it has been cut, the stems will have oval butts whereas if pushed or dressed, the butts will be round

Cut

Uncut

Plate 26 Water reed is stiff and strong enough to be dressed or pushed into shape

If there is exposed wood on the surface at the eaves, has the thatch tended to open where the spars penetrate?
Should there be exposed ligger or cross-spar work at the eaves, the thatch is, as mentioned earlier, most likely to be long straw. However, if this style is used on either water reed or combed wheat reed, perhaps where a new extension is required to match an existing long straw roof, it will tend to open the coat which may, after a few years, show dark lines under the eaves where water is being allowed in.

What is the colour and texture of the thatch under the eaves where it has been totally protected from the elements?
Straw when new is a bright golden-yellow and in unexposed places will retain a certain amount of its colour for some years. When damped with water it will be flexible and bend without splintering. Water reed is darker in colour and less malleable.

The final test is to pull, gently and carefully, one piece of the thatch out from either under the eaves or from the face for close examination. No damage can be caused by the removal of one stem, particularly if it can be done without actually climbing on the roof. Positive identification of cereal straws can be made by examining the ear. The stems of winter wheats are usually hollow, although there are some solid stem varieties such as Capelle.

Plate 27 The final test when identifying thatch is to pull a piece out

41

Clearly there is no one positive test and there are exceptions to every rule and to almost every thatched roof. However, if the guidelines are followed correct identification can be made. Once this major hurdle is overcome it is easier to quantify such things as how long the thatch has been on the roof, and how long it is likely to last before it needs patching, reridging, replacing or covering with wire (or nylon) mesh. Although there are many pitfalls for the unwary there is no reason why it should not be possible for the layman to learn to make an accurate assessment.

Natural deterioration

In general terms, the largest single reason for thatch to deteriorate is directly related to the length of time that moisture is retained on the surface of the coat. Microbiological activity takes place in wet warm conditions, causing the reed or straw to break down. Thus the drier the climate, the more exposed the roof and the steeper its pitch, the longer the material will last.

Any part of the thatch protected from surface water will show little or no sign of deterioration over an extended period. It is fair to say that frequently one finds the original straw base coat still in perfect condition in the roof space of centuries-old cottages.

For some guidelines to deterioration the following should be taken into account:
Deduct 30 to 40 per cent life expectancy for thatch in mild, wet climates — for example the west of England.
Deduct 10 to 20 per cent of expectancy for pitches of roof below 45 degrees down to 40 degrees and, alarmingly, deduct 20 to 50 per cent for pitches from 40 to 30 degrees. Pitches slacker than this will deteriorate with great rapidity.

Longevity will also be reduced by such things as moss and lichen growth which do not allow the free run of water off the roof. A roof surrounded by high trees and constantly in shade, or not exposed to sun and wind, will be similarly affected. (See also Chapter 5 on roof maintenance.)

ESTIMATING AGE

In estimating the age of a thatched roof the variables are limitless, not only because of climatic and structural differences but also because the quality of both materials and thatching work will have a considerable influence. Bearing this in mind, the following figures can be taken as a general indication of the extent of useful life that can be expected:

Long straw: 15–25 years.
Combed wheat reed: 30–40 years.
Water reed: 50–80 years.

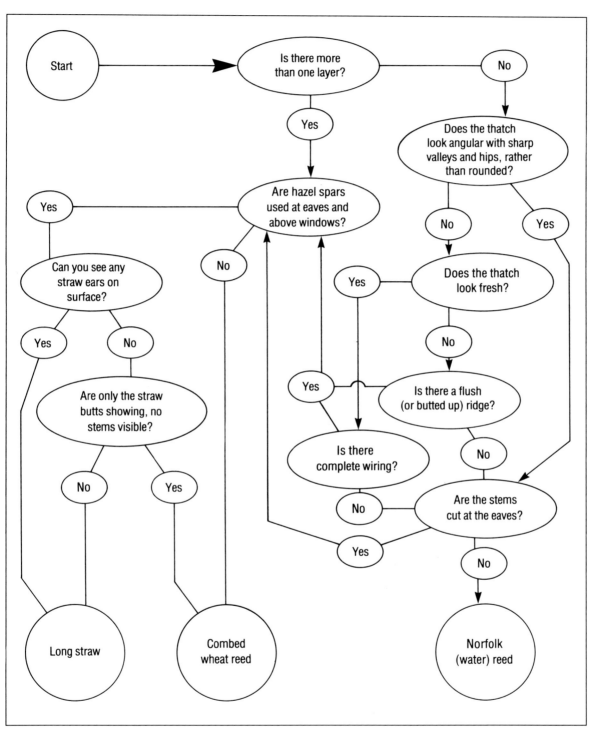

Thatch identification flow chart: remove one stem and follow charted instructions to reach a positive identification

These figures apply to the coat or main body of the thatch, though with all three materials the thatch may require patching to ensure that it lasts its full life-span. At the apex of all thatched roofs is a ridge (see Chapter 4), which may be block cut and patterned, or flush patterned, and either saddled or simply 'butt-up'. The former will last approximately 10–15 years, the latter 6–10 years.

To assess the age of thatch, it is again worthwhile to start another checklist of telltale signs that are noticeable from a distance. For example:

1 Is the colour of the thatch golden-yellow, brown, silvery-grey, black, or are different parts different colours?
2 Are the lines of the eaves and ridge straight and sharp?
3 Are the contours of the roof firm and sharp?
4 Can the wire mesh be seen from a distance?
5 Is the wire on the ridge inches higher than the top of the thatch?

Plate 28 Has the ridge worn away from the wire netting? An obvious sign of deterioration, even to the inexpert observer

6 Are the spars broken or slipping from the ridge or the eaves?
7 Is there any other obvious damage, such as around chimneys, or any other signs which might arouse suspicion?

The following tables give an indication of the state of a thatch at a given age. They are simply guides and the variations of structure, climate, good or bad materials or quality of thatching should be taken in consideration.

Long straw
Years 1–3
1 The coat will be reasonably bright in colour, particularly under the eaves and at unexposed places.
2 The geometry of the roof will not be marred by any form of wear or gulleying.

44

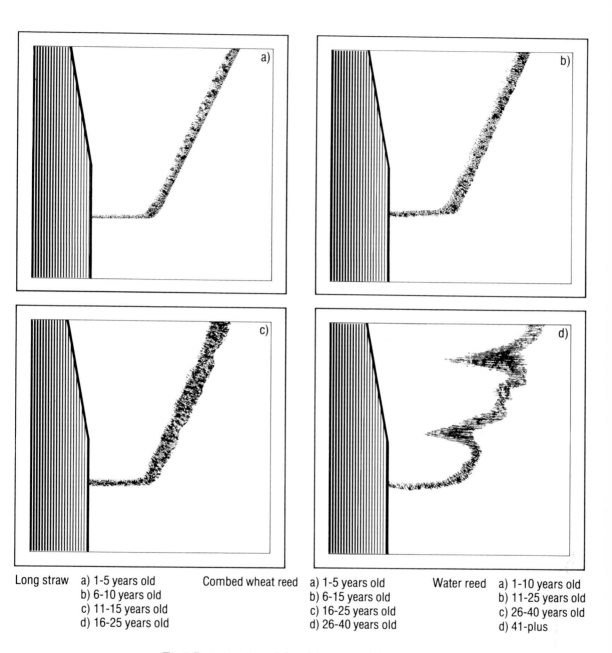

Long straw   a) 1-5 years old   Combed wheat reed   a) 1-5 years old   Water reed   a) 1-10 years old
                b) 6-10 years old   b) 6-15 years old   b) 11-25 years old
                c) 11-15 years old   c) 16-25 years old   c) 26-40 years old
                d) 16-25 years old   d) 26-40 years old   d) 41-plus

Fig 9 Deterioration of thatching materials over time

3 The galvanised wire mesh, either 20 or 22 gauge, will remain unrusted and reasonably visible while still shiny.
4 All exposed spar work will be tight, firm and flush with the coat.

Years 4–8
1 The thatch will take on a much darker colour, particularly towards the end of the period, but will still be yellow, though not bright, under the eaves. When viewed from under the eaves, a dark line perhaps half an inch wide will be apparent along the outer edge, showing the depth of rainwater penetration.
2 The ridge will be showing the first signs of untidiness towards the end of this period.
3 There should be no change to the contours of the roof.
4 Towards years 4–6 of the period, 22 gauge wire will have begun to show signs of rust along the eaves where it was bent into position; 20 gauge will not yet show such signs.

Years 9–12
1 Definite signs of wear begin. Large rusty patches now appear on the surface of the thatch.
2 The ridge will be deteriorating noticeably.
3 Valleys begin to hollow and show signs of wear and there will also be hollowing adjacent to chimneys.
4 The wire mesh begins to separate at the eaves, where even 20 gauge wire is now rusty.
5 Cross spars will be slipping from the ridge.

Years 13–16
1 The coat will be looking worn but will still have a few more years wear. Dark patches start appearing under the eaves.
2 The ridge will either obviously need renewing or be neat and tidy showing that it has recently been replaced.
3 There may be patching in valleys and gulleys by chimneys.
4 The wire may be completely finished or fairly shiny and therefore renewed recently.
5 The cross-spar pattern at the eaves and gables will have almost totally disintegrated or have been replaced and look obviously new.

Years 17–20
There will be definite signs of deterioration in the coat and odd patching will be necessary to extend its life. The original fixings of the courses of straw will possibly be showing on the surface. This is a sure sign that the thatch is within a couple of years of the end of its reasonable and useful life.

Plate 29 Long straw eaves beyond the end of useful life. The outer edge is considerably worn and ragged. The darker patches show the depth of water penetration, and staining down the wall shows that the roof timbers must also be wet

Plate 30 Bright new combed wheat reed in its first year. The surface will gradually darken, though the unexposed cheeks of the windows and areas under the eaves will retain their colour until about the fifth year

Plate 31 Combed wheat reed 6–8 years old. The colour has darkened but the ridge is sharp and intact and the general contours of the roof are good

Combed wheat reed

Years 1–3
As for long straw.

Years 4–10
As for long straw.

Years 11–15
1 There will be no particular signs of wear on the coat work. The under-eaves dark line will possibly be one inch wide on the outside edge.
2 The ridge will obviously be in need of replacement, or will be newly laid and sharp.
3 The wire will have separated at the eaves and be rusting on the coat, or will be new and fairly bright.

Years 16–28
1 The protected area under the eaves will no longer be yellow but dark and dusty.
2 The ridge will have been replaced towards the second half of the period and will once again be showing signs of wear.
3 Valleys and areas around chimneys may need patching.
4 The thatch will have been rewired during the period and the wire will have started to deteriorate again at the same rate as before.

Years 29–40
As with long straw, if the original fixings are visible on the surface of the coat, the thatch is virtually at the end of its useful life. Patching will be

required towards the end of this period to maintain weatherproofing. The reridge and rewire should still be wearing reasonably well and may outlast the main coat.

Water reed

Years 1–12

1 The colour of water reed is darker than winter wheat and therefore changes are slower and more subtle. Even at the end of the period when the coat is quite dark, the colour of the butts under the eaves will not have changed greatly.
2 The ridge will need replacing towards the end of this period and it is here alone that apparent signs of wear will allow a reasonably accurate date to be determined.
3 As a whole, the thatch will appear firm and tight, and will maintain its original lines throughout the period.
4 Water reed is not usually covered all over with galvanised mesh so there is no rusting wire as an aid to dating the roof.

Years 13–28

1 Though there will be no obvious change in condition, the coat will darken, even under the eaves, and the original colour of the reed can only be seen by the removal of a stem. The butts on the face of the coat will be brittle to touch and easily broken.
2 The ridge will need replacing again towards the end of the period.

Plate 32 Water reed 14 years old. The ridge is new but the main coat is still firm and tight

Years 29–40

1 The coat is now quite black, although the stem colour is unchanged three to four inches from the surface. The exposed butts are now very brittle.
2 Reridging will be necessary towards the end of the period.
3 The contours of the roof should still appear totally sound as deterioration is relatively slow with only subtle changes. There is probably no need yet for patching, even in valleys or below chimneys, although the darker areas under the eaves will indicate clearly where future work will be required.
4 All slopes may now be covered in galvanised wire mesh — wire is usually replaced at the same time as the ridge.

Years 41–60

1 Even at this stage, if one piece of reed is removed the colour, with the exception of the exposed end, will be similar to when it was laid.
2 The eaves will become ragged.
3 The coat may show signs of unevenness and slippage in one or two areas and will need attention, particularly in valleys and below chimneys, to maintain its useful life. At approximately years 40–45 one or two course marks may appear (see Plate 33). This is the first major change

Plate 33 Water reed 40–50 years old, with course marks clearly showing wear

in the roof and will give a reasonably accurate guide for dating purposes. Later, fixings will become exposed to the elements as the coat wears down, but it should still be possible to repair and patch to get a few more years' life.

Plate 34 Eaves of water reed, 60 years old plus

SURVEYING

Many surveyors will need to evaluate thatched properties during the course of their work and the following section is aimed specifically at them.

Having positively identified the material by removing a piece, ensure that all parts of the roof are thatched with the same material — it will frequently vary from one area to the next. Careful detection work will now be needed to date the material, following the guidelines given in the tables above. Don't jump to a conclusion but ensure that you have two or more reasons for your decision. Avoid getting on to the roof unless absolutely necessary.

Don't forget outside influences on wear: geographical location, slack pitch, overhanging trees, moss and lichen growths, a north or south facing aspect will all contribute to earlier deterioration both on the surface and under the eaves, in valleys and beside and below chimneys. Beware layers of moss or pine needles — although the roof surface may appear sound the thatch hidden underneath will be damp and deteriorating and even possibly full of gulleys showing advance deterioration.

It is possible to get an indication of depth of coat with either combed wheat reed or water reed by the length of butt visible on the surface. In

Plate 35 *Be careful before making a decision — on the right is water reed, on the left is combed wheat reed*

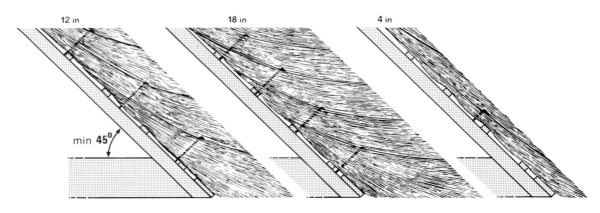

Fig 10 *The pitch of the roof will relate directly to the pitch of the thatch and equally the thickness of the thatch will influence the pitch of the thatch. Thus, an 18in coat of thatch will lie at a much slacker pitch than a 12in coat and therefore a thicker coat will wear more quickly. The thinner the thatch, the steeper the pitch — however there must be adequate thickness of thatch over the fixings — thus a 4in coat of thatch is steeper than a 12in coat, but because the exposed stem length is longer (and therefore wears more quickly) and because there will be very little thatch over the fixings the thatch will not last as long as a 12in coat.*

An optimum thickness for maximum longevity would be between 9 and 15in for water reed and 9–12in for combed wheat reed and long straw

rough terms, if only 25mm (1in) or less are visible the coat is 300–380mm (12–15in) thick; if 40–50mm (1½–2in) are visible it is 230–300mm (9–12in) thick; and if 100–130mm (4–5in) of butt shows it is a very thin coat, probably 150mm (6in) or less. The optimum is 230–300mm (9–12in) as although the thinnest work lies at the steepest pitch to the roof and therefore sheds water quickest, it provides little covering for the fixings and leaves a lot of stem unprotected on the surface. A 460mm (18in) coat may offer more protection to the fixings but it lies at a slacker pitch and therefore wears more quickly than the 230–300mm (9–12in) coat.

Check carefully under the eaves at all points. Dark or wet patches show clearly the depth of penetration of water into the coat and also how close this decay is to reaching the roof timbers. If these telltale signs are halfway between the surface of the thatch and the rafter feet, prompt attention is needed to that area.

Plate 36 Long straw, probably 13–15 years old. These rain gulleys, typical signs of wear, will correspond with dark 'vees' under the eaves showing how deeply the water is penetrating the thatch. Patching will eventually be necessary to allow the roof to complete its full life-span

Plate 37 The valley shows the point of water penetration under the eaves — as yet no problems on this 16-year-old water reed

Plate 38 This 1930s Norfolk reed house appears at first glance to be having a new ridge. Not so — the bottom pattern ligger is being replaced, the block will be recut and the coat dressed all over to make the roof temporarily look a lot tidier, but nothing will be added to its life-span

Plate 39 All timbers over 150 years old must be considered suspect. This cottage in Kent had a three foot thick thatch but when it was removed it was found that there was no structural timber remaining — though the thatch above had kept its pitched shape

If the thatch has galvanised wire mesh on it, check the rusting and discoloration carefully as it is a very clear indication of the length of time that the wire, and possibly the ridge, have been on the roof.

Be on guard for the thatch which has been 'smartened up', perhaps to encourage potential purchasers. Minor repairs (see Plate 38), though they may have only a short-term effect, can to some extent disguise the true age and condition of the roof.

It is not within the scope of this chapter to discuss timber at any length, but it should be pointed out that practically all roof structures over 150 years old are affected by woodworm and their soundness must be considered suspect. However, this is not necessarily a disaster; restrutting from the inside is feasible and the degree of flexibility that thatch has will allow a considerable amount of movement.

Having established age one can roughly estimate how long the thatch may last, but to do so exactly is practically impossible. All that can be said is that a particular material has a life expectancy of n years in a certain geographical location (see page 42) to provide a basis for calculations. It may be necessary to patch from time to time to allow the thatch to last for the maximum period.

Be critical within reason. Remember that thatch is a natural material; there are no measuring tools in thatching, everything is done by eye, and minor variations in the geometry of a roof, though they will not affect its life expectancy, are inevitable.

Let us say there is a scale of 1–10 into which all thatch in terms of quality falls; 10 being perfection and unobtainable, a top score of 9 is more realistic. To take a few examples: course marks, lines across the roof particularly noticeable within the first five years of thatching, would lose perhaps ½ a point at the top end of the scale though they certainly will not shorten the life of the thatch; a variation of 20–50mm (1–2in) over 3m (10ft) on a gable may lose ½ a point; a hollow area in the surface of the coat in a straight piece of roof may lose ½ a point, and so on. The nearer work approaches the top end of the scale, the more obvious irregularities are.

There is great variation in thatching standards; not all roofs attain 9 on the scale and nor can such high quality be reasonably expected in every case. Obviously, the price paid will be reflected in the end result. If a roof was thatched very cheaply, inevitably, it will not last as long as one thatched more expensively, but this does not necessarily imply poor workmanship.

As a final note — on more than one occasion professional surveyors have been threatened with litigation by dissatisfied owners some years

Plate 40 There are few roofs as bad as this. Combed wheat reed in long straw style — not two months old and already slipping off and leaking. The signs are obvious: loose course marks, particularly on the hips; no saddle on the ridge. Very poor thatching that will have to be replaced in a year or two

after their original thatch report. In such cases the first step is to check that the complaint is reasonable, for example, ensure that vermin have not contributed to the deterioration. If there is any doubt, a second expert opinion must be obtained.

REGIONAL THATCH

An experienced thatcher if transported blindfolded to any rural part of England would be able to tell where he was by the style of the thatch. Materials also have some bearing though they are far less localised today than they were in past centuries. Norfolk reed roofs were once confined to East Anglia but now appear in all parts of the country. Market demands have contributed to the spread of combed wheat reed, once exclusive to the Westcountry, and examples are found in most counties. On the other hand, long straw, formerly the most common thatch, is fast dwindling in popularity; although cheaper than water reed or combed wheat reed it has a much shorter life. It also takes longer for the thatcher to prepare for the roof and, as the cost of this must be passed on to the homeowner, in the long term it represents less value for money. There will probably come a time at the end of this century when long straw can be afforded only by purists and it may well become a style of the past.

There has been an interesting cross-pollination of thatching styles as thatchers use materials according to their individual skills, regardless of regional tradition. In the west of England, for example, water reed for coating work is sometimes fixed with hazel spars and shaped to resemble combed wheat reed.

Regional thatches are constantly changing features. A type of pinnacle built, say, in Essex cannot strictly speaking be regarded as the county style. It will have been developed by one thatcher who has passed on his skill to others and, because the majority of thatchers stay fairly close to home, this particular pinnacle will become associated with a certain area. A decade hence, a new master thatcher may develop a new feature which, if it has sufficient following, will in turn be recognised as the local style.

Although there are overt regional variations there are also similarities in that all ridges in the United Kingdom are formed in the same thatching material as the main roof — with the exception of water reed, when sedge is also used.

This however is at variance with other parts of Europe, where not only is this typical English ridging never found, but the alternatives are many. In Holland and Germany there are clay ridge tiles; in Denmark and Sweden, 4 × 4in oak logs laid over a very coarse straw ridge; in France, turfs; and in Northern France, (Brittany and Normandy), iris corms in mud are fixed to the ridge.

41▶

42▶

43▶

◄44

Plate 41 Devon twist ridge. But the ridge is not the only feature which suggests that this roof is the work of a Devon thatcher: the shape of the eaves and the gables, the material (combed wheat reed) and the use of a shearing hook on the surface are all signs for the sharp eyed

Plate 42 This cottage, thatched in combed wheat reed, is in Hampshire. But the elaborate block-cut patterned ridge and the style of the windows and eaves could also be attributed to Wiltshire and Berkshire

Plate 43 The wrap-around gables and the ridge pinnacles of this long straw thatch are instantly recognisable as styles from Essex and Suffolk

Plate 44 Essex and Suffolk — long straw. The ridge is block cut, patterned and saddled, though the scalloped skirts are perhaps only an inch thick

Plate 45 Even when old and fast wearing towards the end of their lives, Essex/Suffolk thatches are unmistakable

▼45

46▶

47▶

48▶

Plate 46 Somerset/Dorset style of ridge pinnacle — a very ornate roof, well thatched in combed wheat reed ▲49

Plate 47 Another variation in pinnacle design from Somerset, on a flush ridge in combed wheat reed

Plate 48 A common feature of Devon thatch is the slackness of the roof pitch, seldom greater than 45 degrees, which must add to the problems of early degradation

Plate 49 Even a wall shows a Wiltshire thatcher's skills — flush wrapover ridge and clean lines

Plate 50 An old straw coat in Berkshire. Note the window shapes which are very similar to the Hampshire style (see Plate 42) though the material is different ▼50

51▲

▼52

◄53

Plate 51 Water reed house in Denmark. The ridge is formed with loose straw and covered with wire mesh which, in turn, is pinned down by small oak logs joined at the top. Note the lightning conductor on posts running down the hip
Plate 52 In Brittany, thatched roofs are still occasionally found. Here a Breton thatcher is covering an old roof with rye straw
Plate 53 Thatch in Holland is almost exclusively water reed but it is ridged with clay tiles which are concreted into position
Plate 54 These African thatchers will be familiar with the materials and methods used in Britain but they will finish the roof with a tin or concrete ridge

◄54

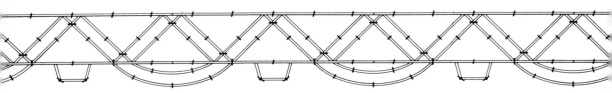

4
Thatching Methods

Although techniques vary according to the materials being used and to traditional regional styles, all thatchers follow the same basic procedure of starting work at the eaves and progressing up the roof to the ridge in overlapping courses. Some may lay the strips horizontally across the roof, others may work vertically taking a series of courses upwards known as 'stulches'. The material is fastened firmly to either the timbers of the roof or to a base coat of existing thatch, and most of the fixings are interchangeable between water reed, combed wheat reed and long straw.

One of the thatcher's most difficult tasks is to lay the material in the correct direction to shed rainwater from every part of the roof without it penetrating to the timbers. He has to turn his thatch 90 degrees from one gable to the other, through valleys and around hips and windows, while maintaining the pitch of the roof so that water will flow from butt end to butt end down to the eaves.

There are no definitive rules in thatching and a skilled craftsman will choose the method most suitable for any particular set of conditions and requirements. No two roofs are the same and from time to time the thatcher will need to be flexible in his approach to the job, perhaps occasionally combining one method with another to achieve the best results.

LONG STRAW

Long straw is delivered to the thatcher in loosely tied bundles after threshing has removed the cereal from the ears (see Chapter 2). These bundles are opened and pitchforked into loose layers to form a 'bed'. Each layer of the bed is wetted and the straw left roughly parallel, although not aligned precisely, with heads and butts at either end.

The thatcher (or his labourer) then begins to prepare the bed in 'yealms' or layers. This is back-breaking work which necessitates the thatcher leaning forward and with both hands pulling straw from the bottom layer of the bed (see Plate 56). He slowly moves backwards until one complete yealm, a few inches thick, is neatly formed with the individual straws parallel to one another on the ground. The process leaves the thatcher with cleaner hands than any soap can. Each yealm is then split into

Fig 11 Unlike tiles or slates, thatch guides rainwater off. A thatcher must learn how to change the direction of the thatch — 45 degrees off gables — into valleys and off hips etc

Plate 55 A mixture of materials and fixings. On the right is water reed laid with mild steel rods and steel thatching nails; on the left, combed wheat reed laid with spars and a straw bond

smaller yealms, approximately 100mm (4in) thick by 450mm (18in) wide (see Plate 57). These are tied with twine and carried on to the roof in a hazel fork known as a yealm holder.

Starting at the eaves, the yealms are tied firmly with tarred twine or polypropylene on to the first batten. This first course must be secured tightly not only to give added weather-proofing over the eaves, but also to create a resilient base which allows subsequent courses to be fixed firmly; it also makes the job of trimming (cutting) the eaves easier when the thatch is complete.

If the long straw is being fitted to a new roof the next course (the brow course) is now laid on top of the eaves course. Approximately halfway up the yealm the twine is passed through the ears of the course below, under a batten and tied firmly. There are several variations on how the twine is fastened around the batten. It may be a 'two-man' task with the thatcher passing a threaded needle to his apprentice inside the roof, who unhooks the twine and rethreads the needle when the thatcher pulls it back. A mechanical needle operated by one person is commonly used in Holland.

However, it is more usual for long straw to be laid over an existing thatched roof, which requires the removal of at least one layer of the old rotting thatch. The old roof is then prepared by having any gulley filled

Plate 56 Handfuls of straw are pulled from the bottom of the bed to form yealms

Plate 57 Each yealm is split into smaller yealms which are bound with twine ready for thatching . . .

Plate 58 . . . and carried on to the roof in bundles

Plate 59 A long straw coat being laid in stulches on top of old thatch

Plate 60 Preparation of old thatch prior to recoating. The eaves and gables have been stripped down to the first batten

in with new straw to create a firm, flat foundation. The better the preparation, the easier it is for the thatcher to make a fine finish. The eaves and gables are sometimes stripped to expose the first batten (see Plate 60) before the eaves course is fixed as already described. This may appear to be additional unnecessary work, but if the preliminary stage is completed properly the following courses are easier and quicker to lay, last longer and look better. It is not essential to strip the eaves or the gables on every roof; it depends largely on the quality of the existing material.

The brow course is sparred on to the old thatch, which is sandwiched between this and the eaves course. Spars are either hazel or willow rods, split and sharpened with three cuts from a billhook (the minimum number of cuts to produce a point). The spar is twisted in the middle (rather like wringing a piece of cloth) so that the grain of the wood laminates allowing the spar to bend without breaking (see Plate 62). The

Plate 61 *Spars — split, sharpened and tied into bundles of 250, awaiting collection from the coppice by the thatcher*

Plate 62 *A spar twisted and bent in the middle ready for use*

giant 'hairpin' is pushed through the straw approximately halfway up its length in a direction parallel with the ground. Despite being protected from rain by overlapping layers, spars must not be pushed into the thatch running downhill for, should any water penetrate it will run down the straight edge of the spar and further into the thatch, thereby increasing deterioration. A spar used correctly holds very firmly, not only because of its natural tendency to spring outwards but also by friction.

A handful of the straw is then lifted from behind the spar, brought horizontally across the course and sparred again at about 150mm (6in) from the first spar. The process is repeated along the length of the course creating a straw bond. (See Plate 70 on page 75, which shows a straw bond on combed wheat reed — the method is identical.) This is the traditional method of fixing straw on to a base coat of old thatch, but instead of a straw bond a hazel rod is often used, again being sparred at 150mm (6in) intervals.

The courses continue up to the top of the roof where one or more ridge rolls (see page 76) are fitted to maintain the pitch of the roof and also to give a very firm foundation for the ridge.

An exposed hazel ligger or cross-spar pattern is sparred along the eaves line and vertically up the gables. This pattern, although aesthetically pleasing, is not just for cosmetic purposes. It is structurally important as

Plate 63 The side rake is pushed into the thatch an inch or two above the line of the intended cut

Plate 64 Eaves neatly sliced through the straw to give a beautiful shape and finish

it tightens the eaves and gables and allows for easier trimming. As explained in Chapter 3, cross-spar patterning of the eaves is a practical aid to identification of thatching material, even from a long distance.

When all the courses are firmly in place a side rake is passed down the coat in a combing motion. This gives a neat finish to the coat, ensuring that the straw runs parallel and that most broken lengths are removed. The eaves are raked and cut to shape (see Plates 63 and 64); the straw must be wet for the sharp cutting hook to be completely effective.

The ridge is then laid (see page 82) and the job is nearly complete. The final tasks are to cover all slopes with galvanised wire or plastic mesh to prevent vermin damage, and to clear up the considerable amount of debris which will have accumulated.

COMBED WHEAT REED

The bundles of combed wheat reed, like long straw, are also delivered to the thatcher straight from a trusser. However, this material has passed through a comber which has removed all the broken straw and leaf (see Chapter 2). This debris accounts for almost one-third of the total weight of the original harvest and partly explains the increased cost of the material over long straw. In addition to this, the butts are all at one end

Plate 65 Full hip in long straw, showing the flowing lines and the direction in which the straw must lie to shed water by the most effective route

and the ears at the other, which saves a lot of the ground work necessary with long straw.

The bundles are butted down (or some would say up, depending on the vagaries of the English language) to make sure all the butts are flush at the end, and approximately an inch is cut off to give a neat appearance. The bundles are usually wetted (although this is not essential) and taken on to the roof. The process is then very similar to that used for fixing long straw.

The old thatch, if there is one, is prepared and the eaves and gables are stripped completely. Eaves wads or 'bottles' — tightly tied bundles of thatch — are then tied individually on to the first batten (see Plates 68 and 69) and the brow course is fixed with spars, which makes a sandwich

(above left) *Plate 66 Combed wheat reed. The bundle on the left is as delivered, the one on the right has been butted down*

(right) *Plate 67 Before the wheat reed bundles are taken to the roof the butts are clipped to give a neat appearance*

(left) *Plate 68 Wads or 'bottles' of tightly tied thatch are made up to be laid for the eaves course*

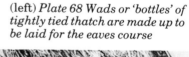

Plate 69 The ears of the bottle go under the old thatch, which is sandwiched between the new courses as the coat is formed

of the old thatch between the two new courses. Again, either a straw bond (see Plate 70) or hazel rods can be used to secure the thatch along its length.

Combed wheat reed is dressed in courses up the roof with a grooved wooden bat called a 'leggett', leaving only an inch or two of butts visible on the surface of the coat (see Plate 71). This is a far more precise operation than long straw thatching and leaves the reed in its finished state.

In some areas, particularly the Westcountry, a shearing hook is used to obtain the finished surface and to get rid of unwanted irregularities (see Plate 72). However, the section cut from the straw is the toughest (closest to the butt) and therefore some of the weathering qualities are removed. More importantly, shearing changes both the shape and the pitch of the reed ends. This means that water can remain on these areas for longer than on unsheared butts and therefore microbiological action can take place for longer periods.

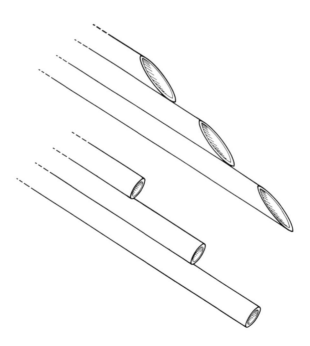

Fig 12 By cutting the butts on the face of the coat of combed wheat reed, not only is the toughest part of the wheat stem removed, but the shape of the butts becomes oval instead of its original round shape. This probably holds moisture for longer than the uncut stems and may add to early degradation of the roof

Plate 70 Straw bond on combed wheat reed

Plate 71 Dressing combed wheat reed with a leggett

Plate 72 Shearing a wheat reed coat for a perfect finish

Plate 73 Making the ridge rolls; (right) *Plate 74 A series of ridge rolls secured above the ridge board to maintain pitch and provide a firm foundation for the final course*

Ridge rolls are used at the apex to maintain the pitch and give a firm foundation for the ridge itself (see Plates 73 and 74).

Combed wheat reed is used widely on 'newbuild' thatch, particularly extensions to existing cottages which have been thatched traditionally with long straw. It blends well with long straw and has a similar shape and softness, with the advantage of being a longer lasting material and therefore more cost effective. In these cases the thatch can be laid combining the methods used for both long straw and water reed.

Initially eaves wads are individually made and tied to the first batten. The brow course and subsequent courses can then be tied to the battens in the same way as long straw (see Plate 75). More commonly used are either 6.35mm (¼in) mild steel rods or hazel rods laid along the courses, approximately halfway between the butts and the ears, and held with long steel thatching nails or crooks inserted through the thatch to touch the rafters. These crooks are driven home with a hammer 13mm (½in) to 25mm (1in) into the timber to fix the course firmly — not so firmly that the straw or

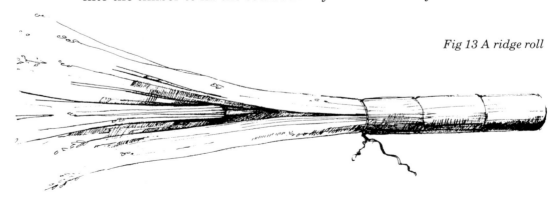

Fig 13 A ridge roll

Plate 75 On a newly-built roof all courses are tied tightly to the battens. The trainee practising here has secured the brow course with a straw bond and spars, but thatch is more commonly fastened to bare timbers with rods of mild steel or hazel, and nails

Plate 76 It is most important to create a weatherlap between bundles of thatch. The thatcher is lifting a section of the course just laid to ensure that his next bundle will be partially covered

Plate 77 Combed wheat reed eaves being trimmed with a pair of shears

rod is broken or indeed so far into the timber that the rafter splits. Crooks vary in length between 100mm (4in) and 350mm (14in) and should be correctly chosen for the particular course. As a guide to crook length, if the course is 300mm (12in) thick the nails used will be approximately 230mm (9in) long. As the courses near the ridge, the nail length will increase as the reed thickens away from the roof timbers over the ridge rolls. Neither the mild steel rods nor the nails deteriorate any more quickly than the thatch as they are protected from the rain by the overlapping courses (see Plate 76).

The eaves and gables are cut either with an eaves hook or knife or, more commonly today, with a pair of two-handed shears (see Plate 77). Galvanised wire mesh or nylon netting can be fitted over the roof if required to prevent damage from vermin.

WATER REED (NORFOLK REED)

The thatcher receives his load of water reed cleaned and ready for use. He sorts it into bundles according to length and quality: the longest bundles will be laid at the lower courses, with the exception of the eaves course, and the shorter ones will follow as the thatching approaches the ridge. There are always uses for long unruly bundles such as in ridge rolls or backfill (see page 81), particularly in valleys, and thus there should be little or no wastage.

If an existing thatch is to be replaced all old material must be removed exposing the roofing timbers.

It is at this stage that expense over and above the thatching contract price can occur as almost certainly there will be need to attend to the roof structure, which may not have seen the light of day for half a century or more. It is usual for the battens to require renewing, along with the kick-rail at the rafter feet. Occasionally a rafter or two will need replacing, but the houseowner can then be sure of the soundness of the structure. Battening will usually be carried out by a thatcher but it is advisable to call in a carpenter to work with the thatcher where major structural timber replacement is necessary.

With the roof prepared and all old thatch off-site and disposed of, the thatcher starts work from the eaves. Instead of making eaves wads or bottles as with the other materials, he takes a whole bundle and butts the ends down on the ground or against a spot board. He then shapes the butts off to 45 degrees by tilting the bundle; this ensures that the underside of the eaves course will be horizontal when the bundles are tied in place. The eaves course is tied under great tension (see Plate 80) and the first batten

Plate 78 A long straw roof is stripped to bare timber prior to being rethatched in Norfolk reed. The old thatch was about five feet thick above this window which appeared to have been formed as an 'eyebrow' until stripping revealed it as a dormer

Plate 79 *The bundles of water reed selected for the eaves are butted down and angled at approximately 45 degrees*

Plate 80 *The eaves course is tied very firmly to the first batten. (Once the bundle has been secured the binder twine, visible at the bottom of the photograph, will be removed)*

Plate 81 *A mild steel rod is placed approximately halfway between the butts and the ears of the water reed and secured by a thatching nail or 'crook'*

must therefore be secured well — usually with 80mm (3in) wire-cut nails and not the 50mm (2in) nails with which the remaining battens are fixed.

Until the 1960s almost all water reed was fixed with hazel rods and steel thatching nails. However, for economic reasons the hazel rods have been replaced largely by 6.35mm (¼in) mild steel rods (see Plate 81). Although hazel can be produced without great cost from a coppice or hedgerow it takes time and labour to cut, whereas relatively cheap, uniform, straight lengths of steel rod can now be bought direct from manufacturers. An alternative method of securing each course on to the battens with twine was also used extensively in bygone years.

It is true to say that a thatched roof will last as long as its weakest point. Generally speaking, with water reed it is the fixings that deteriorate first. Steel rods, providing they are kept dry, will outlast hazel, which is subject to worm and is usually suspect by year 50 (see table, page 51).

Each course is dressed with a leggett, which for water reed must be faced with metal; the grooves of a wooden leggett would be worn flat very quickly by the reed butts. Traditionally, flattened horseshoe nails were driven into the wood (see Plate 82) but today a reed leggett is more likely to be surfaced with extruded aluminium or half-circles of copper pipe secured with staples.

Whilst the courses are being dressed, small handfuls of backfill reed are pushed under the ears of the previous course. This not only serves to give

Plate 82 A Norfolk reed leggett with horseshoe nails driven into the hard wood face

an attractive finish to the underside of the thatch, but also allows the reed to slide smoothly over the battens when being dressed into position.

A valley needs considerably more backfill than any other part of the coat. Because of the slackening of the pitch in a valley and the fact that there is a greater volume of space to fill under the thatch than on the surface, large quantities of reed, laid ears down and butts up, are packed beneath the courses to prevent the ears of the face reed from falling below the level of the butts. This clearly would create the worst kind of problem as water would run into the roof rather than off it. Conversely, a hip needs very little backfill.

Because water reed is so much stronger than the other thatching materials, the eaves and gables are not cut to shape but are dressed with a leggett (see Plate 85). The ridge is fixed in position and the job is done. Galvanised wire mesh is not usually fitted to new water reed, although the ridge, which is of sedge or straw or combed wheat reed, is frequently covered as the materials are softer and more vulnerable to attack. In the 40th or 50th year of the life of water reed it is advisable to wire the coat as the fixings can begin to weaken and allow vermin to cause damage.

THE RIDGE

At the apex of all thatched roofs is a ridge. It is the final piece in the 'jig-saw' and protects the fixings of the top course of thatch below. Spanning the thatch on either side of the roof, the ridge provides a weathertight saddle to shed rainwater on to both slopes without ingress at the apex, and gives a decorative finish.

Each ridge has to be individually planned and constructed according to the building and type of thatching materials used. There is no hard-and-fast rule. The last ridge roll may be on top of the skirts; the ears of the skirts may be folded over the ridge roll or knuckled under it, and so on — all methods are acceptable and vary depending on the thatcher's skills, regional style and the structure of the roof.

The first step in laying a ridge is to secure rolls of thatch on top of the ridge board to maintain the steep pitch, to act as a buffer against which the roof reed or straw may be pushed, and to produce a firm foundation on which the ridge can be built. Over these rolls at least one course of thatch is laid; the final stages will depend on whether the ridge is to be block cut or flush.

Block-cut patterned wrapover (or saddled) ridge

If a block-cut patterned ridge is being built, skirts will be laid on the top course and secured on both sides of the apex with hazel or willow spars. Some of these spars may be only temporary, to be removed when the saddle is fixed.

Plate 83 A valley being formed with a 'dutchman'

Plate 84 A hip being formed in water reed, showing a half course tied to the steel rod of the course beneath. This makes a tight firm hip which cannot lift in high wind

Plate 85 Water reed eaves are not trimmed to shape but dressed with a leggett

86▶

87▶

88▶

◄89

◄90

Plate 86 Thatch for the ridge saddle is yealmed and stretched
Plate 87 The thatcher takes a manageable amount of material and bends it in readiness
for saddling over the skirts and ridge rolls
Plate 88 Saddle in place, the liggers are fastened on top, the thatch is combed neatly
down into position and the cross-spar patterning is laid
Plate 89 Bent and twisted 'hairpin' spars are pushed horizontally into the thatch to hold
the decorative ligger pattern in place
Plate 90 Finally, the skirts are cut to shape. There are no measuring tools — it is all done
by eye

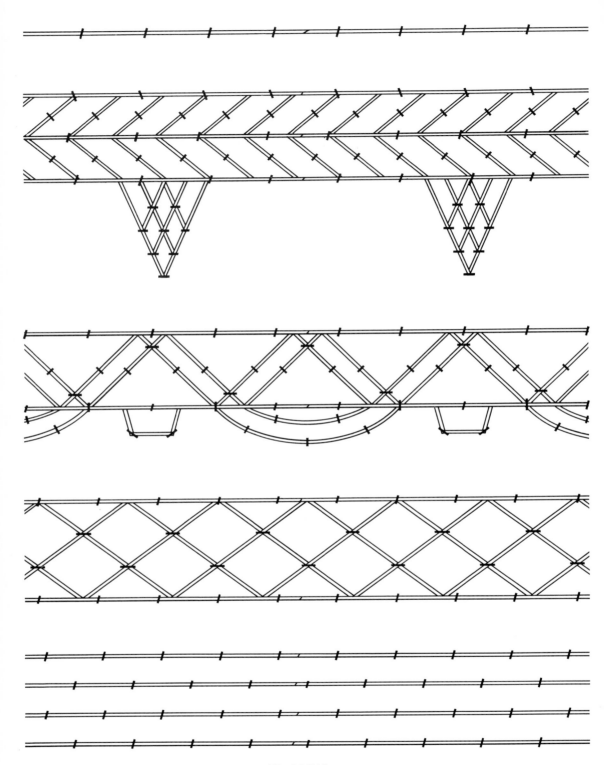

Fig 14 Ridge patterns

87

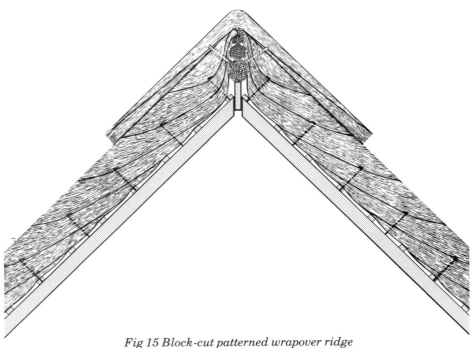

Fig 15 Block-cut patterned wrapover ridge

The saddle, or yealm, of ridging thatch is laid over the top from one side to the other and fixed to the skirts with a pattern of spars. Finally, the skirts are cut to set off the roof to the best advantage. Many different cuts are used and include scallops and 'vees', either blocked out or reversed, clover-leaf designs or simple, gentle curves. The arrangement is generally left to the thatcher's discretion and he will fashion it to express his own individuality, knowing that it is the capping which invariably attracts most attention. Possibly up to a thousand different ridge patterns or styles exist and relatively small variations in cross sparring, numbers of liggers or thickness of ridge enable a particular thatcher's work to be clearly identified by his fellow craftsmen.

The materials used for the ridge vary according to the main thatch. Sedge blends well with water reed and is normally used for the wrapover; the skirts can be either sedge or straw. With a straw roof, straw skirts and wrapovers are usual.

Neither the material nor the thickness of the skirts bear relevance to the lasting quality of the ridge. The wrapover (saddled) ridge will last 10–15 years whether flush or block and whether the block is 25mm (1in) or 50mm (2in) thick.

Flush wrapover (or saddled) ridge
A flush ridge is one where the wrapover, or saddle, fits straight on to the top course of thatch (see Plate 92); there are no skirts and hence no cut

Plate 91 Block-cut patterned, saddled ridge: Norfolk reed coat; combed wheat reed skirts; sedge wrapover

Plate 92 A flush ridge with a typical Westcountry finish on the hipped end. This thatched wall has an entire roof in miniature — eaves bottles; brow course; possibly a course above the brow; ridge rolls; and cross sparring

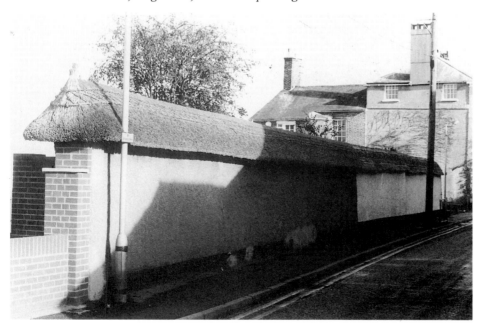

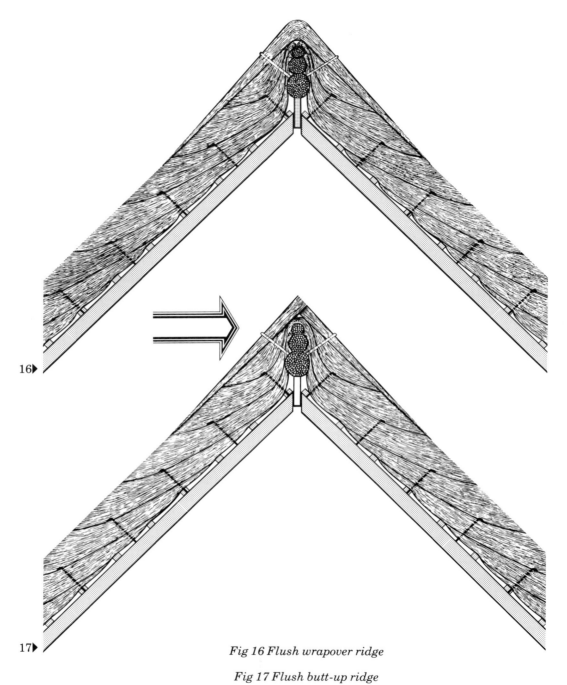

16▶

17▶

Fig 16 Flush wrapover ridge

Fig 17 Flush butt-up ridge

Fig 18 Block-cut, patterned, butt-up ridge

Fig 19 Flush Devon twist ridge

Fig 20 Block-cut, patterned, Devon twist ridge

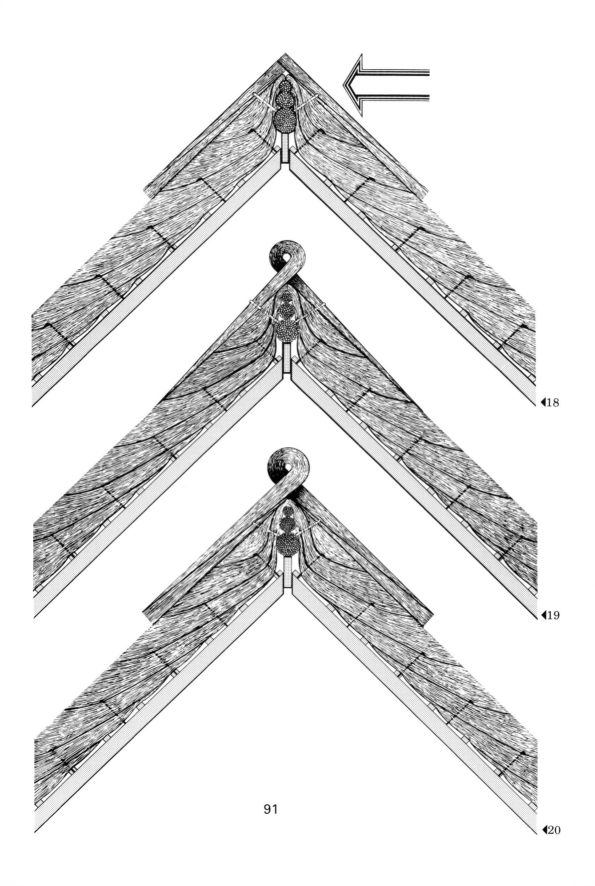

◄18

◄19

◄20

Plate 93 Westcountry block-cut patterned, butt-up ridge in combed wheat reed on a water reed coat

patterns. This classic simple finish is a favourite with many thatchers though most people prefer to see something more elaborate. Its life-span will be the same as that of the block-cut ridge — about 10–15 years.

Butt-up and twist ridges

In the Westcountry a 'butt-up' ridge with no wrapover is popular; for this the butt ends of wheat reed are fixed pointing up with the weatherside butts being slightly higher than those on the other side (see Plate 93). This method works well on a steep roof but it does not last as long as a saddled ridge; 6–10 years would be realistic for this type of ridge, whether block cut or flush.

Another style of ridge sometimes found in the Westcountry — the Devon twist ridge — is made by twisting and tying straw round a pole which is removed before the sections are placed on the roof like a cap (see Plates 94 and 95).

WIRE MESH

The reason for wiring a roof is to prevent birds and rodents from damaging the thatch. Plastic or nylon netting certainly helps prevent bird damage but it is of little value as protection against rats or squirrels, which make short work of it.

Plate 94 Devon twist ridge — block-cut patterned and saddled

Plate 95 A beautiful example of a Devon twist ridge on a well-head

Either 20 or 22 gauge 19mm (¾in) galvanised wire is preferred. It has a small enough mesh to keep out birds but will not spoil the look of the thatch.

The approved method of covering the thatch is to start at the top and roll the wire down one side only. It can then be twisted together at the top with the corresponding drop on the other side. The wire is twisted in the same way to join the seams. This not only ensures no unsightly overlaps but also stretches the wire tightly over the thatch leaving fewer bulges. Most important, in the event of fire, the fire brigade can easily drag off the wire as the joins give way under pressure like a zip fastener.

The 22 gauge wire is the thinner and lighter mesh and should have a useful life of 10–15 years, the same as the ridge. It may need attention from time to time and will certainly need a little patching at the eaves to see a full 15 years. However, 20 gauge will last the life of the ridge without attention. Being heavier it is more difficult to fit and in being more obvious to the eye is perhaps less attractive than the lighter gauge.

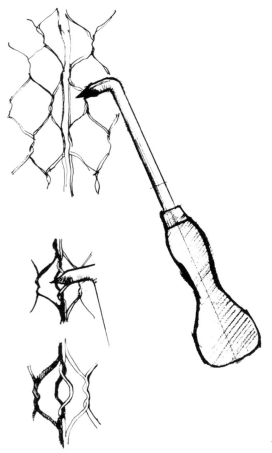

Fig 21 Wire being twisted together

94

FLASHING

If there are chimneys in the roof they must be sealed round with lead or cement flashing, once the ridge and wiring are completed, to shed rainwater on to the thatch.

Lead is efficient but expensive both as a material and in terms of the skilled labour required to fit it. It will last 30–40 years — certainly far longer than the ridge. When a ridge is replaced it is not always possible to fit a new one to the exact dimensions of the old and the lead flashing also will then probably have to be replaced, despite having many more years of life. However, lead has advantages. If fitted properly its appearance enhances the roof; it sheds the water 150–300mm (6–12in) on to the thatch; and galvanised wire is easily removed from underneath it if the thatch should ever need patching in the area of the chimney.

Cement on the other hand is inexpensive, and if benched properly with adequate materials can also look attractive. It does not suffer any movement and is not therefore liable to the cracking associated with cement flashing on tiled roofs. When the time for a reridge arrives the cement can be knocked off the chimney and a new ridge and new flashing formed. Wire netting is cemented into the flashing and will have to be cut away if entry to the thatch is required.

DISPOSAL OF WASTE MATERIAL

Disposal of waste during and after thatching is always a problem. Burning on site should be avoided if possible and some public liability insurance underwriters specifically define a policy as null and void if damage is caused as a result of this practice.

If the thatcher can find someone with a use for waste thatch, he is fortunate. Normally he must dispose of his own waste materials and this cost is taken into account when a quote is given for rethatching.

5
Maintenance and Repair

Natural wear and tear of thatch can be accelerated by a large number of problems, most of which are within the power of the houseowner to overcome.

It is advisable to obtain a professional surveyor's report on the condition of the thatch at regular yearly intervals. This should cover every facet of the thatch, estimate the roof's life expectancy and also suggest precautions which should be taken, allowing the owner to contain minor problems before they deteriorate and require major repairs.

Any inadvertent damage, for instance a ridge crushed during the course of chimney repairs, should be attended to at the earliest opportunity. Window cleaners, painters and decorators need to be particularly careful on thatch — not only with ladders, but also with their feet. Often the damage is superficial and requires only minor cosmetic attention from a skilled hand to redress the coat and straighten the wire.

Plate 96 Inadvertent damage to the ridge caused during repairs to the chimney

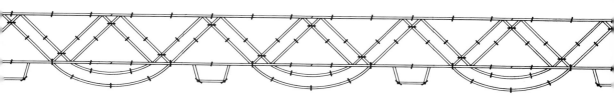

ATMOSPHERIC CONDITIONS

The chances of a thatch achieving its maximum life-span are affected by, above all other factors, the rate at which microbiological activity breaks down the material (see also the section on natural deterioration, page 42). Given that this activity can take place only where there is water, it is essential that the thatch should remain dry for as long as possible.

The question is occasionally posed: 'Why should the north side of the thatch last longer than the south when it is permanently wet and seldom out of the shade?.' The phenomenon is not as noticeable in the south of England as in the Midlands and East Anglia, and the answer probably lies in temperature rather than moisture alone. Thus, although the north slope remains permanently wet it is also too cold for the microbiological activity to work at the speed it will on the warm south-facing slope.

The pitch of the roof and the geographical location are not easily altered. However, overhanging trees which block sunlight can be cut back; and moss and lichen growths (see below), which similarly keep light and air from the thatch, and also retain water, can be controlled.

FUNGAL AND PARASITIC GROWTHS

A temperate climate, high humidity and clean air conditions, such as are experienced in the west of England, are ideal for breeding fungi that begin the decomposition process in thatch. To combat this early degradation, chemical treatments have been developed, such as an organic heavy metal compound, toxic to biological growths. This adheres to cellulose which is the main constituent of straw and reed. The treatment gives the best results when applied as a preventive measure to new materials; it can also be used to destroy existing growths in older thatch but the disadvantage of this is that much of the toxicant is lost with the growths as they perish and wither away. Copper wire sparred to the bottom pattern ligger on a ridge has for many years been considered a good deterrent, as carbonates and hydroxides of copper in dilution are spread over the surface of the thatch whenever it rains and help to discourage fungal growth.

Chemical sprays can also be used to fight other parasites such as lichen and moss both by killing existing growths and by preventing the development of new ones. The life expectancy of these spray treatments is influenced by prevailing conditions. If the roof is in a damp, shaded position the moss will re-establish itself faster than it would on a more favourable site. However, treatment will normally last for several years. Weathering will gradually remove the treated moss, though if very dense or entangled in the wire it may take longer to clear or need to be removed by hand.

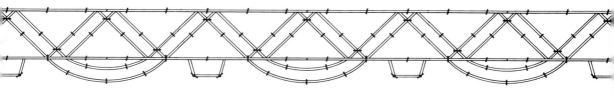

Plate 97 Eight-year-old combed wheat reed with copper overflow pipe, showing clearly the different rate of deterioration where carbonates and hydroxides of copper have been spread over the surface by rainwater

Never attempt to climb on a roof to spray moss or fungi — call in a specialist. The thatch will be wet and soft, and clumsy ladder work will do it more harm than is caused by the growth.

PESTS

Birds, particularly in spring, may damage the thatch while nesting; the common sparrow is a persistent culprit. They can pull whole lengths of straw or reed out of the roof and the hole formed follows the line of the thatch, ie upwards and inwards. This does not create leaks, because the water continues to be shed down the surface of the coat, but a general weakness is caused around the affected area when a substantial wedge has been removed. The gap should be repaired and all slopes covered with

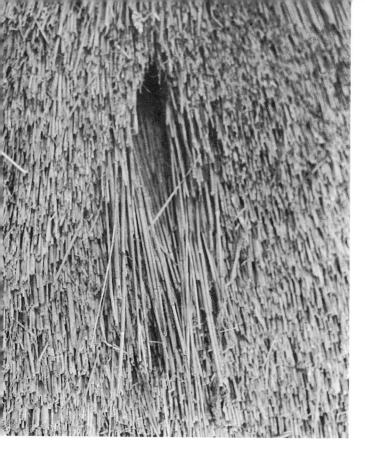

Plate 98 Birds pull out whole lengths of straw and leave a hole which is relatively easily repaired

Plate 99 Long straw, approximately 15 years old — the eaves wire has separated and has not been attended to, allowing considerable bird damage. The hole on the hip face is also caused by birds. The problem could have been remedied easily two or three years ago; now it is of major concern as the eaves timbers are open to the elements and damp and rot must be getting into the overall roof structure

19mm (¾in) galvanised wire mesh. If the roof is already wired check for breaks, generally accompanied by bird droppings, and if the damage is in reach repair it, if out of reach call in a thatcher.

Although bird damage is relatively easily and inexpensively repaired, rodents present greater problems. Pests such as rats, mice and squirrels do not pull, they chew, and they can move under the thatch in any direction. The resulting damage is difficult and expensive to repair and will be a job for the thatcher. If in doubt as to what is causing the problem, check the length of the straw or reed that will have fallen on the ground from the suspect area: whole lengths indicate birds; short, chewed lengths, 100–200mm (4–8in), are the work of rodents. If rodents are identified call in your local pest control experts to remove them as quickly as possible. Check that the roof cavity has no obvious access points, as squirrels and rats enjoy investigating such holes and if they do get in they could cause extensive damage as they try to get out again through the wire netting.

Plate 100 Thatch chewed by rodents. This problem frequently occurs days after rethatching and rewiring have been completed because a rat or squirrel has been trapped in the roof

PREVENTION OF FIRE

There is no treatment which will render thatch non-combustible although there are certain products on the market (see below) which can afford a limited degree of protection against fire. However, normal, commonsense precautions can reduce the risk to a minimum.

Have the electrical wiring throughout the house checked every five years by an expert. Many fires have been started by faulty central heating systems or worn-out wiring. The Electricity Board will often conduct a free visual check and give you an estimate should any work be necessary. If you are leaving your home unoccupied for more than a few days, switch off and drain the hot and cold water system.

If you have an open fire or wood-burning stove, make sure the chimney is swept regularly — at least twice a year. Check the pointing in the chimney breast, particularly in the roof void. Chimney lining methods have improved over the years and it is now possible to line any aged chimney breast from the inside. An inflatable 'sausage' is dropped down the chimney and filled with air, then wet cement is poured down between the sausage and the chimney. Make sure the diameter is large enough for an open fire or wood burner if that is its intended use. When the cement has set the sausage is deflated and the chimney made safe.

Spark arrestors can be fitted to chimneys as an additional safeguard; these are galvanised wire cages which extend from the top of the chimney pot (advise the manufacturer of the inside dimensions of your chimney pot when ordering) and prevent large sparks and pieces of burning paper from falling onto the thatch. The wire cage does tend to soot up over a period, which can effect the draw of the chimney, and when the chimney is cleaned the cage inevitably gets dislodged and will need to be replaced.

Never take a naked flame, or even a hot-air blower, into the loft to unfreeze pipes — they will eventually thaw if the hatch is left open. In many old thatched roofs the atmosphere in the roof void is tinder-dry and highly combustible.

Check which way the wind is blowing when you light bonfires, and ask your neighbours to do the same. At barbecues remember to damp down the fire when cooking is finished; a slight change of wind direction could rekindle the flames — several disasters have been caused in this way.

Keep a dry-powder fire extinguisher in the kitchen and several water or CO_2 extinguishers around the home, and have an outside hose on a reel permanently connected to the mains. A sparge pipe (a long, perforated sprinkler) can be laid along the top of the ridge and connected to a mains water supply at a stopcock. However, the system will have to be drained in winter and, because of the construction of thatch, has only a limited effectiveness. As each piece of reed or straw is hollow it carries its own oxygen supply; it is also laid in a fashion designed to shed water. So, in the

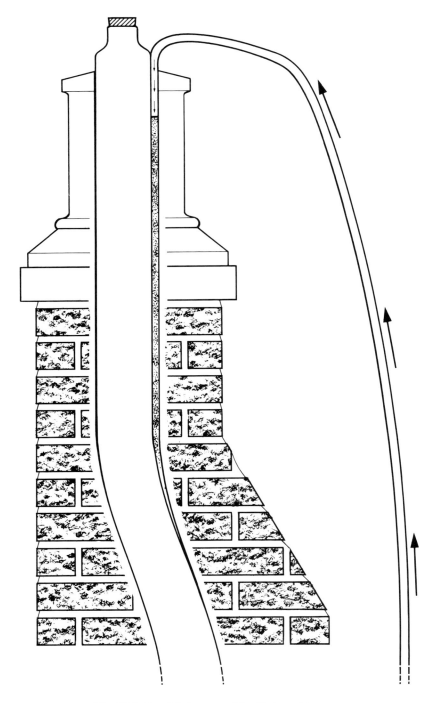

Fig 22 Inflatable 'sausage' for lining chimneys

unfortunate event of a fire, water from the sparge pipe will flow down the outside of the roof while the fire continues to burn below the surface. This system could be improved greatly if it were to be combined with a high-density water mist in the roof cavity, as both temperature reduction and oxygen starvation would be effected. (This suggestion was put to insurance underwriters some years ago and was not accepted on the grounds that further damage would be caused by water — however, there are opportunities here for inventiveness.)

Fire retardant treatment

This consists of a chemical water-based solution of salts which is injected by a multi-headed spray-lance into the thatch. When the chemical drys, the individual straws or reeds are left coated with a fire-resistant deposit which helps to prevent the spread and penetration of flames. Weathering causes this protective deposit to wear off the thatch at the top of the ridge and the outer inch or two of the surface, but it is thought the retardant will remain active in the body of the thatch for 10 to 15 years. However, this method has a limited value as the chemical will not reach every part of the thatch and unless there is access to the loft cavity, so that the underside can be treated, a major area will remain vulnerable.

The greatest protection can be achieved by dipping the bundles in retardant prior to thatching. This is best done on site, with no more material being treated than can be laid on the roof in one or two days, as if reed or straw is immersed in any liquid and stored horizontally it is subject to rapid microbiological action. Recent research has looked into the possibilities of vacuum impregnation and kiln drying to overcome this problem but unfortunately both processes would greatly increase the cost of thatch.

New developments are being made constantly and there is little doubt that shortly there will be a chemical which will reduce combustion rate dramatically, not be prone to leaching, and have added herbicides to prevent moss and lichen growth — all at a reasonable price.

Barrier protection

There are several products on the market which can be used for lining the roof, before the thatch is laid, to restrict the spread of fire. One such material is Barrier Foil 341, a heavy-gauge aluminium foil specially selected and tested for its combination of strength and fire resistance; unlike many composite foils, it contains no flammable constituents. This is fastened directly to the rafters by battens; during thatching it is inevitable that the foil will be holed in many places but such damage will not have a significant effect as the foil's usefulness as a fire retardant is, in any event, limited. Eighty per cent of its value is as a thermally reflective insulator and before thatching is completed it acts as an efficient weather-shield, allowing other trades to continue their work or even making it possible for the house to be lived in.

The use of Barrier Foil 341 will reduce the insurance premiums payable on otherwise high-risk thatched properties, and has also proved to be an asset when planning permission for thatched buildings or extensions could be jeopardised by concern about potential fire risk.

There are other barrier products, such as Master Board, an asbestos-free product with fire retardant properties, which give a considerably greater degree of protection than foil — however, they have their disadvantages. The materials are rigid and therefore difficult to handle. If being fitted on top of rafters they screen the line of the rafter from the thatcher who might drive his nails into the wrong place and easily

Plate 101 Barrier foil being fitted to a new roof. It is laid under the battens and over-lapped in the same way as roofing felt

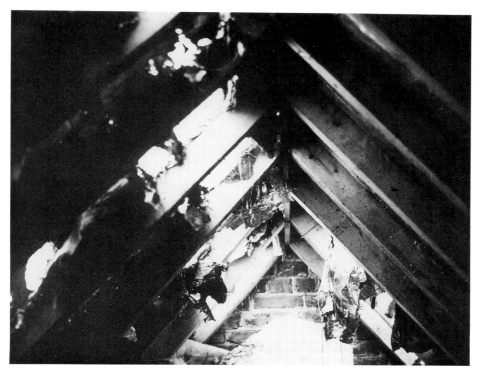

Plate 102 Fire damage inside the roof cavity. The thatch and battens were badly burnt but barrier foil, although almost totally destroyed, stopped the rafters from catching and the main timbers remained unscathed

damage the board. In these circumstances it is advisable to fix a strip of small beading on top of the Master Board into the right-hand edge of each rafter: when the thatcher pushes his nail through the thatch he will feel the beading with the nail point and know that he is on top of the rafter.

Lightning conductors

Many thatch owners are worried by the idea of lightning starting a fire. And when one considers that a lightning flash can be as much as five times hotter than the sun's surface, it is sensible to treat the subject with respect.

For a fair zone of protection it is necessary to erect a conductor above the highest point of the roof and to supply a conducting strip down to a good earth. As the majority of thatched roofs have wire netting stretched over them, it is a comfort to know that this also assists in safely routing the lightning, but the wire must be connected to an earth strip. The recommended size of the earth strip is at least 10mm (⅜in) diameter.

Copper is the most highly conductive material and it will not corrode. Aluminium can also be used and although it is not as conductive as copper, when compared size for size, this can be compensated for by using a larger section.

Whatever treatment or equipment you use to prevent the spread of fire, do not wait to see how effective it is if the thatch is alight — call the fire brigade immediately.

SEASONAL MAINTENANCE

Possibly the most useful task to be carried out in the spring is a close inspection of the eaves for bird damage (see page 98). Obviously, this is relatively easy on single storey and low cottages, but even higher eaves are generally no problem.

Summer is as good a time as any to have such work carried out as chimney pointing, erection of television aerials, maintenance of electricity and telephone services and so on. Providing the thatch is dry, less indentation will occur but remember that if a ladder's stiles are not lying flat on the roof they can damage the eaves. So make sure the angle is right; it also helps if the ladder is cushioned or bound by sacking or similar material.

Before the end of the year it is wise to take steps to guard against the devastation that winter can cause. Check that roofs and chimneys are sound and that drain gratings are clear so that water can run away. Pipes and tanks should be insulated, but leave the space beneath the water tank free so that warm air can reach it.

Plate 103 Do not allow a ladder to dig into the thatch at the eaves (see left) — lay it evenly over the whole surface area of the thatch as illustrated on the right

Snow, being nature's cellular foam, adds to the insulating properties of a roof, both muffling sound and keeping in heat. There is little need to remove it, though there may be some temptation to scrape snow from the eaves in an attempt to prevent heavy blocks detaching themselves and damaging shrubs. The job should be undertaken with extreme caution, for if you should catch an implement, such as a rake or hoe, in either the wire or wooden spars, you may dangerously loosen the thatch. Snow, unlike rain, can blow upwards, especially around draughty corners and it would be sensible to visit the roof space, if access is possible, to look for visible signs of snow or wet patches. The problem can usually be remedied by packing glass wool in any gaps.

Although a flash flood cannot be prevented, some precautions can be taken to stop the creep of water over the threshold. As thatched roofs do not have gutters fitted, any rainfall tends to puddle the ground immediately adjacent to the walls causing soil erosion and splash marks. A way of preventing this, which will both clear up this area and provide somewhere to stand when cleaning ground-floor windows and carrying out eaves maintenance, is to dig a ditch around the property, the centre of which should be plumb with the eaves edge. The ditch need only be 300mm (12in) deep and about 370mm (14in) wide to cope with most roofs. It should be filled with pea shingle, as the name implies, a pea-sized aggregate.

DIY REPAIRS

Repairs to the surface of the thatch should be carried out only by a professional, but do-it-yourself repairs to eaves and netting are not too difficult.

The materials required for mending a hole in the eaves are: a bundle or two of long straw or combed wheat reed or water reed, depending on the material of the roof; some lengths of hazel or willow, about 600mm (24in) long and up to about 25mm (1in) in diameter; some tarred twine or old baler twine. Lay down enough of the new straw so that when firmly grasped its diameter at the ears end will be a fair fit in the hole. Tie the bundle at two points — say 100mm (4in) and 250mm (10in) from the ears. Before pulling the twine really tight, push the length of hazel or willow down the centre of the bundle, from the ears end, leaving a good half of the rod sticking out; this end can be sharpened.

Push the bundle up into the hole (see Plate 104), making certain you do not trap any nestlings, and tap it firmly in with a mallet. If it has been made the correct size it will stay firmly in position. Any stray ends can be trimmed with ordinary garden shears.

This type of repair can only be carried out at either the eaves or the barge ends; if attempted on the main roof area it could cause a leak.

You can now go ahead and repair the wire.

Plate 104 A tightly tied bundle of new thatch is forced up into a hole. Within a short time the colour will fade from the patch and the repair will be invisible

Plate 105 Wire mesh separating at the eaves — a simple DIY task for the houseowner

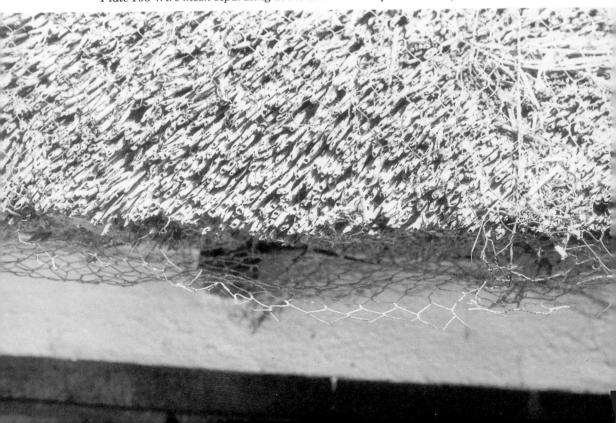

INSURANCE

The insurance of thatched property, because of the fire risk, is more expensive than for tiled or slated roofs; the cost of the annual premium would be approximately double that for non-combustible roofs. The owner, or potential owner, would be well advised to seek the services of a specialist organisation, as their rates will be substantially lower than those offered by the general insurance market which still looks upon the risk of thatch with great suspicion.

It is important to remember that thatched homes should be insured for the full rebuilding cost — the market value of any property is not a reliable indication of this. Advice may be obtained by contacting a local surveyor or architect, or indeed the organisation arranging the cover.

6
Building for Thatch

This chapter is intended primarily for architects and builders, as building a roof is a major undertaking beyond the skills of the average DIY enthusiast. However, it is hoped that the houseowner will be provided with some useful ideas and tips.

Both metric and imperial measurements are given in the text, although a craft industry such as thatching will cling stubbornly to the imperial system and architects and builders may work solely to the metric system. All dimensions in the line drawings are in imperial units and brief reference to the text will supply the metric equivalents.

Plate 106 Design for simpler thatch. The buttressed gable negates the need for the material to be turned through 45 degrees to shed water away from the gable wall

Plate 107 An extension to a cottage showing the first gable wads tied in position. The structure comprises: a 75 × 75mm (3 × 3in) sawn arris rail at the rafter feet; 100 × 50mm (4 × 2in) rafters at 400mm (16in) centres; 50 × 25mm (2 × 1in) battens at 225mm (9in) centres. An unusual feature is the gable finish, where instead of a barge board, the battens have been extended 50–100mm (2–4in) past the barge rafter, and a hazel twist has been formed to create the kick of a barge board — a traditional central and southern English style

Plate 108 The new combed wheat reed coat is married course by course into the old long straw and when dressed into position matches well with the thickness of the old coat. The left-hand gable is 'bottled-up' together with the eaves; the ridge rolls are started at the ridge board; the new coat is brought right-handed away from the old and the reed is turned into the valley

Plate 109 *The eaves and the right-hand gables are 'bottled-up' and the thatching begins. The entire roof is being tied course by course on to the battens*

Plate 110 *Extension completed — old and new ridge levels meet and coat levels match; within a year or two, when the colour fades, their join will be virtually invisible*

ROOF CONSTRUCTION

It is advisable to set the pitch at about 50 degrees. This is not due to the weight of the material, which is in fact not overheavy, but rather to facilitate drainage. Dormer roofs and eaves-window roofs should be at least at a 45 degree pitch, if possible.

Smaller span roofs

For a 5m (16ft 6in) roof with a clear span a simple form of truss is required. The trusses should be set between 1.8–2.4m (6–8ft) apart. Rafters, ties, collars and diagonals should be 100 × 50mm (4 × 2in). The diagonal members should be notched so that the purlins will be held at right angles to the rafters.

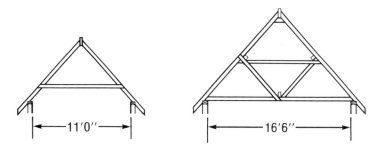

Fig 23 Smaller span roofs

The size of purlin is dictated by the distance between trusses and will vary from 125 × 50mm (5 × 2in) to 175 × 50mm (7 × 2in). Binders will vary from 125 × 50mm (5 × 2in) to 150 × 50mm (6 × 2in).

All ceiling joists should be spiked to the binder to prevent sagging. Binders can be omitted if there is a convenient structural wall at or near the centre of the span. Up to a 3.3m (11ft) span, the construction can be of a simple collar type with the collar set in the bottom third of the roof; 100 × 50mm (4 × 2in) ceiling joists can act as collars if conveniently positioned. All rafters must be bird-mouthed over the wall plates.

Valley
A 175 × 40mm (7 × 1½in) lay board is placed over the rafters of the main roof. The jack-rafters are attached to this and the ridge can be set between the twin rafter members of the truss.

Medium span roofs

The truss illustrated in Figure 25 is suitable for a 7.2m (24ft) span. Ridge collars, diagonals and bottom ties should be 100 × 50mm (4 × 2in), hangers are 75 × 25mm (3 × 1in). With a span of this size the ceiling joists require

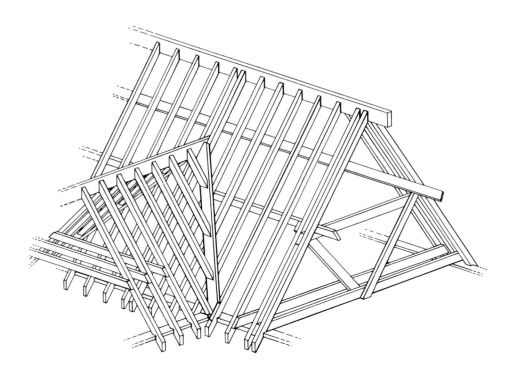

Fig 24 Structural framework of a valley

support in three positions if they are to be kept at 100 × 50mm (4 × 2in). This truss provides for three binders which can be omitted whenever a convenient structural support is available.

Valley
With large and equal spans, a conventional 175 × 32mm (7 × 1¼in) valley rafter should be used. Jack-rafters should then coincide as far as possible. Where rafter spacings of the two roofs are different, a lay board should be employed.

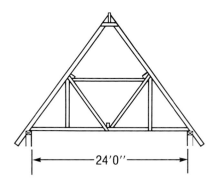

Fig 25 Medium span roofs

114

Ridge

Presuming 100 × 50mm (4 × 2in) rafters and a 50 degree pitch, the ridge plate should be 225 × 32mm (9 × 1¼in) and the upstand of the ridge should be 50mm (2in). The top batten should be placed 50mm (2in) from the ridge; thereafter battens should be spaced at 225mm (9in) centres.

Details at eaves

Vertical fascia and close boarded soffit

This is constructed with a 375mm (15in) fascia held by 50 × 35mm (2 × 1½in) bearers and hangers. The hangers are spiked to the rafters.

Open eaves type

The fascia board should be 30 × 300mm (1¼ × 12in) and grooved to take a 6mm (¼in) tongued and grooved boarded soffit. The soffit bearers should be 50 ×35mm (2 × 1½in) and are fixed to 50 ×35mm (2 ×1½in) plates which are plugged to the wall.

Close boarded raking eaves

The roof is finished with a 75 × 75mm (3 × 3in) tilting fillet. The overhang is infilled with eaves boards and battens and then rendered underneath to prevent vermin getting into the thatch. Unlike the close boarded raking eave and the vertical fascia and close boarded soffit, the top cavity is infilled with expanded metal and mortar.

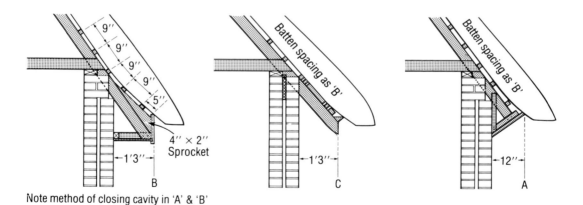

Note method of closing cavity in 'A' & 'B'

Fig 26 Vertical fascia and close boarded soffit

Fig 27 Open eaves

Fig 28 Close boarded raking eaves

115

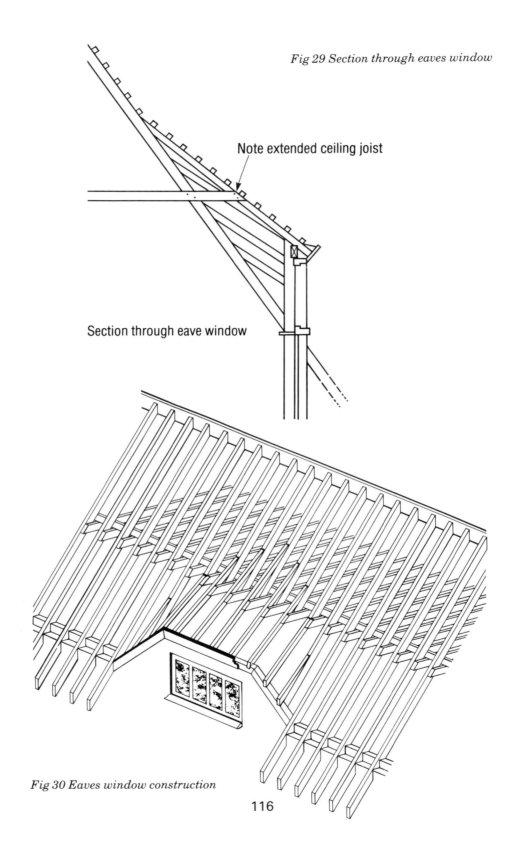

Fig 29 Section through eaves window

Note extended ceiling joist

Section through eave window

Fig 30 Eaves window construction

116

Eaves windows

These are often necessary due to the steep pitch of the roof and the deep overhang of the eaves. The windows can be held in a brick spandrel above the normal wall plate. The wall plate is continued through the spandrel to provide a support for the untrimmed rafters. These are further secured by 75 × 35mm (3 × 1½in) spacers. The top of the wall cavity is closed with expanded metal and cement, and capped with a 75 × 50mm (3 × 2in) wall plate.

The ceiling joists above the eaves window can be extended beyond the rafters to offer an extra securing point for the 75 × 50mm (3 × 2in) rafters forming the roof over the window opening. These rafters are laid in a staggered formation to provide a curved seating for the thatch. The eaves treatment illustrated (see Figures 29 and 30) joins on to a standard eaves type at the bottom of the spandrel.

Verges

See Figure 31.
In both cases illustrated the barge board should upstand the batten by 35mm (1½in). The top of the cavity may be closed by slates bedded in mortar with the batten passing over this.

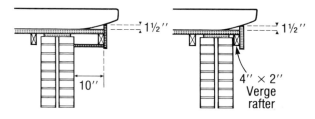

Fig 31 Verges

Built-in purlins should not project beyond the wall into the verge. Also the last rafter is set approximately 25mm (1in) from the inside edge of the brickwork.

Dormer windows

The construction of the dormer roof is similar to that of the eaves roof except that in the example illustrated (see Figures 32 and 33) 75 × 50mm (3 × 2in) ceiling joists have been incorporated to make a flat ceiling above the window aperture. At the foot of the dormer window, rafters are trimmed with a 200 × 50mm (8 × 2in) upstand. The bottom of the sill should be a minimum of 450mm (18in) from the structural roof level. As with verge details, a fascia is required with an upstand of 35mm (1½in). It is important that the pitch should be at least 45 degrees and on no account less than 40 degrees.

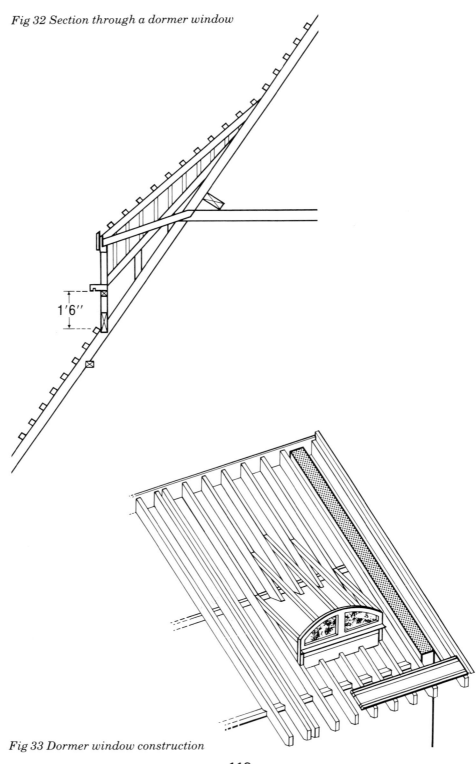

Fig 32 Section through a dormer window

1'6"

Fig 33 Dormer window construction

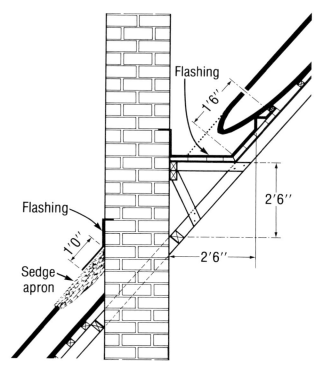

Flashing

Flashing

1'6"

2'6"

2'6"

1'0"

Sedge
apron

Fig 34 Chimney flashing — box gutter

Chimney flashing

The tilting fillet should be 750mm (30in) from the chimney (see Figure 34) and a minimum of 300mm (12in) above the bed of the gutter. This fillet should be 50 × 75mm (2 × 3in) and the gutter bed and upstand should be 25mm (1in) tongued and grooved boarding. The substructure consists of 75 × 50mm (3 × 2in) bearers, struts and plates. The rafters below and above the chimney should be trimmed into either 100 × 50mm (4 × 2in) or 100 × 75mm (4 × 3in) trimmers dependent upon the load they have to bear.

Care should be taken that the gutter discharges above the level of the thatch and that the pargeting to the lower portion of the chimney is not lower than the thatch.

Guttering

Gutterings are not common on thatched roofs, although there is no reason why they should not be fitted. Perhaps the biggest disadvantage is that they have to be removed when rethatching takes place, as they interfere with ladder access; and they do need constant cleaning to remove collected debris.

119

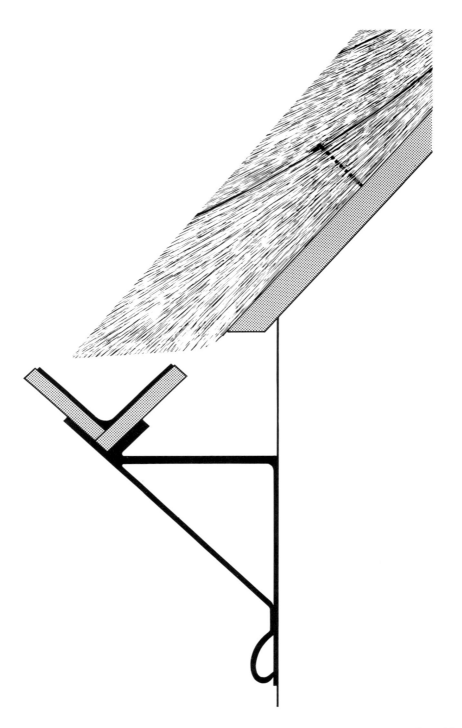

Fig 35 Guttering and bracket. The opening at the mouth of the gutter must be wide enough to cope with several inches of wear over many years

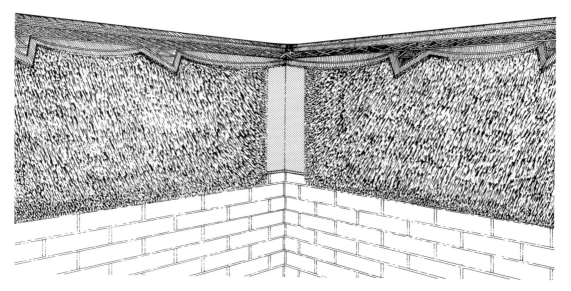

Fig 36 *The combination of a tiled or leaded valley with thatch. The thatch does not turn into the valley but rather is vertical on the roof. The water is then shed into the valley. This is a much simpler, cheaper and longer lasting valley configuration*

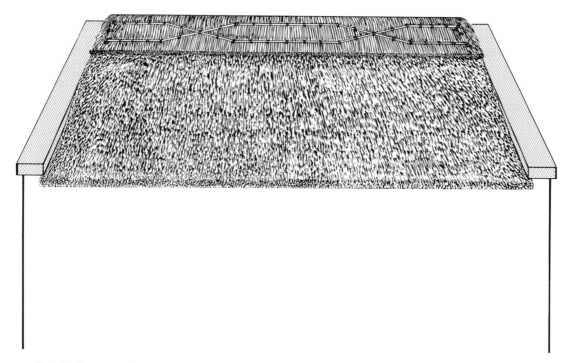

Fig 37 *Buttressed walls do not create a roof configuration requiring thatch to move through 90 degrees from one gable to the other. The thatch is vertical at all parts of the roof — again creating less costly thatching which is simple in construction and long lasting*

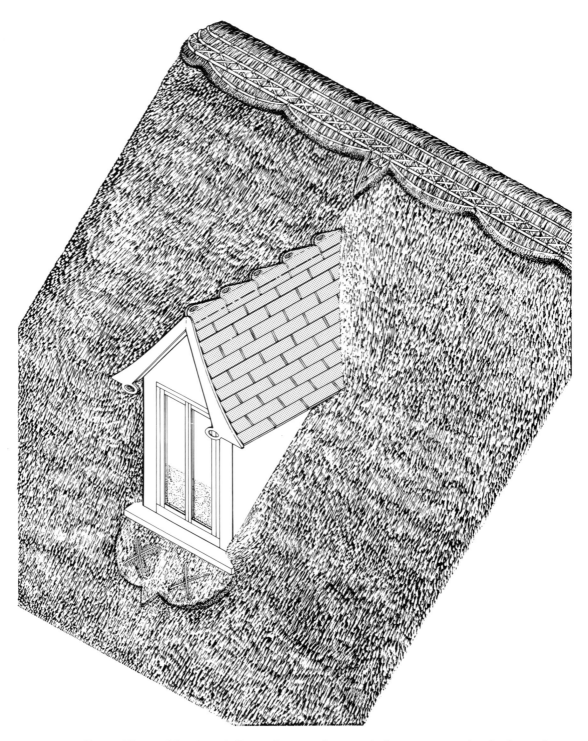

Fig 38 The combination of tiles or slates on dormer windows creates a simpler form of thatching

The collecting gutter must be wide enough to catch water, not only when the roof is newly thatched but years later (perhaps 50 years in the case of water reed) when the coat has worn back several inches. The width of the gutter should be approximately 9in (225mm) to allow for the wearing from new thatch to old thatch. The iron brackets must be substantial and the wooden trough either lined with tar or treated in some way to prevent it rotting.

Simplifying thatch

There are many modern adaptations to thatch which provide a simpler and cheaper alternative to traditional thatching practices. These include the construction of tiled or leaded valleys, buttressed walls and the use of tiles or slates over a dormer window (see Figures 36, 37 and 38).

ESTIMATING QUANTITIES OF THATCHING MATERIALS

Thatchers, like most other roofers, measure their work in 'squares': 1 square = 9.3sq m (100sq ft). An estimate of the materials required, once the dimensions of the roof have been calculated (see page 124), will be based on the quantity of reed or straw, plus items such as tarred twine and nails, needed to thatch each square.

Long straw

Approximately 1 ton of long straw will cover 4 squares at a thickness of 200–300mm (8–12in). Each square will require approximately 200 spars to fix it if the thatch is being laid over an old coat, or perhaps 450g (1lb) of twine if a new roof is being covered. The quantity of wire netting needed can easily be calculated; however, add 10 per cent as there is always unavoidable waste when it is fixed round windows, hips or valleys, or under the eaves.

Combed wheat reed

Combed wheat reed generally is denser than long straw when fixed and 1 ton will cover approximately 3½ squares at a depth of 225–300mm (9–12in). It will require about 200 spars per square if it is a coating job. A 300mm (12in) coat of combed wheat reed on new timbers will require approximately sixty 225mm (9in) nails, 30m (100ft) of steel rod or 450g (1lb) of twine per square. Additional longer nails must be taken into consideration for the top two or three courses.

Water reed

Water reed is measured not by weight but by the bundle or by the fathom. Roughly 80–100 bundles of most continental reed will achieve a 300mm (12in) coat of thatch on each square. Norfolk reed tends to vary in size and it would be better to assume a minimum of 100 bundles to the square. Austrian reed, which measures 1m (40in) circumference of the bundle, 30cm (12in) up from the butts, should be considered approximately 3 times the size of all others. Approximately one hundred 225mm (9in) nails, 30m (100ft) of 6mm (¼in) mild steel rod and a small amount of either tarred or polypropylene twine are required per square.

Ridging

There are such wide variations in ridge styles that it is difficult to suggest average quantities of materials required. However, assuming that the saddle will be 75mm (3in) thick over the top ridge roll and skirts for a block-cut patterned ridge 75mm (3in) thick when sparred and cut out, a 6kg (14lb) bundle of long straw or combed wheat reed should cover the following distances, including both sides of the ridge:

Block-cut saddled ridge:	300mm (12in)
Flush saddled ridge:	900mm (36in)
Block-cut butt-up ridge:	450mm (18in)
Flush butt-up ridge:	1,200mm (48in)

These figures could be 50 per cent over or under depending upon the roof, the materials used and the thatcher.

Numbers of spars and liggers also vary enormously and a highly decorated double-diamond pattern with 4 liggers on each side could take 50 spars per foot run.

Measuring the roof

Newbuild thatch

The length of the wall plate and the length of rafter multiplied together will give you the area of one side of the roof. However, 10 per cent must be added to each dimension — ie eaves length and ridge-to-eaves — before multiplying. This allows for approximately 300mm (12in) of thatch to extend beyond all timber dimensions. Do not multiply eaves length by ridge-to-eaves and multiply the result by 2 for both sides of roof, and then add 10 per cent — your calculation will be 10 per cent out (this percentage will vary depending on size of roof).

Thus if eaves length (ie barge board to barge board) is 9m (30ft), and kick rail to ridge board is 4.5m (15ft), your calculations to allow for 300mm (12in) thickness of thatch over the timbers is 10 ×5m (33 × 16ft 6in) (both increased by 10 per cent) × 2 for both sides ie approximately 100sq m (1,088sq ft).

Recoating

Greater reliance must be put upon the thatcher to arrive at an accurate estimate of the area to be recoated on an existing roof. The amount of stripping required to reach a firm foundation on which measurements should be based will vary considerably according to the condition of the existing thatch.

Assuming the roof carries a reasonable coat of thatch and that the amount of old thatch to be removed will be replaced by approximately the same amount of new material, then eaves length multiplied by ridge-to-eaves is reasonably adequate. However, if there is any doubt about the extent of the stripping, or if very little needs to be removed, extend the eaves length measurement to include the finished thickness of both barges. Similarly, add to the ridge-to-eaves measurement the thickness of the eaves.

These measurements apply not only to regular rectangular roof surfaces but also to half-hipped and full-hipped roofs.

For a circular roof, measure the distance from the top of the ridge down the surface of the thatch and round and under the eaves to the wall. Multiply this measurement by half the circumference.

BUILDING REGULATIONS

The Building Regulations (B4(2); fire spread; roofs) can present a formidable hurdle, which must be overcome before work commences on site. Table 1–3 of the section of the guidance document (B2/3/4) issued by the Department of the Environment relating to fire spread deals specifically with thatch, and is so tightly drawn that the majority of thatching proposals are likely to contravene its terms, unless a relaxation is granted by the relevant district council. If the council officers are not willing to accept such responsibility, plans for thatching may have to be shelved. However, an appeal can be made to the Department of the Environment; the exercise need not be costly and, depending upon the circumstances of the particular case involved, success in obtaining a relaxation is not too difficult to achieve.

How stringent are the regulations? If the building has a cubic capacity of not more than 1,500m³ (1,960yd³) and if the proposed area of thatch is more than 12m (approximately 40ft) from all boundaries of the site, then there will be no contravention of Regulation (B4(2)). Thus detached buildings on plots exceeding 0.1ha (¼ acre) can escape, as long as they are centrally placed within the plot and have a cubic capacity of less than 1,500m³ (1,960yd³). However, all buildings of greater cubic capacity, regardless of their distance from the boundaries, will be affected by the regulation.

Unfortunately, our rural heritage dictates that cottages, barns and other thatched buildings are clustered together. In such circumstances the building to be thatched is unlikely to be more than 12m (40ft) from all boundaries of the site. It is important to note that if a boundary is a road frontage, the distance is taken from the centre of the road. The regulations were not dreamt up by a lover of thatched villages!

No doubt the fear of fire spreading from one thatch to another accounts for the stringency of the regulation, even though the preventive measures now taken against fire risk are extremely effective. Indeed, the risk has itself diminished, with the reduction in the number of open fires, and the disappearance of steam-driven vehicles such as traction engines (involving the burning of combustible materials) from our country roads.

If the area to be thatched is less than $3m^2$ ($32ft^2$) then the relevant distance from the boundaries of the site reduces to 6 metres (20 feet).

However the 6 metre rule, if not as formidable as the 12 metre rule, is nevertheless still difficult to overcome, because the permissible area of thatch is so small and has to be separated from existing thatch by a 1.5m (5ft) strip of a material of limited combustibility. Imagine part of a thatched extension separated from an existing thatched roof by clay tiles or slate!

Extract from Building Regulations B4(2) fire spread; roofs

Description of building	Designation of covering of roof, or part of roof	Minimum distance from any point on a boundary			
		Less than 6m	At least 6m	At least 12m	At least 22m
1 Detached or Semi-detached house with a a cubic capacity of not more than 1,500m³	Thatch or wood shingles	☐	●[1]	●	●
2a – Terraced house 2b – Detached or Semi-detached house with a cubic capacity of more than 1,500m³	Thatch or wood shingles	☐	☐	☐	☐

● Acceptable
☐ Not Acceptable
[1] The area of the part of the roof should not be greater than $3m^2$ and it should be at least 1.5m from any similar part, with the roof between the parts covered with a material of limited combustibility.

Some councils are sufficiently realistic to appreciate that there are important reasons why the Regulations should be relaxed. In most cases, there are three key issues which need to be debated:

1 The extent of infringement. This will be different in every case and will depend not only upon the proximity of the site's boundaries to the proposed area of thatch, but also on the proximity of nearby buildings — especially if they, too, are thatched.

2 The degree of fire hazard. Most owners or would-be owners of thatched property are sensible enough to realise that with appropriate precautions — the injection of the thatch with fire-retardant materials, the use of barrier foil, safe electrical wiring and the provision of extinguishers etc. — fire risk can be virtually eliminated. An application seeking a relaxation of the regulation would be aided greatly if the houseowner's proposals for taking such preventative measures were carefully spelt out.

3 The planning and amenity issues. A great deal of sympathy can often be drawn from the council's planning department: planners love thatch. Furthermore, to extend an existing thatched cottage in tiles or slate can be to turn an attractive dwelling into an incongruous feature of countryside and village. If planning permission is granted for the proposed additional thatch, the case for allowing a relaxation of the Regulations is much enhanced.

So, if your plans to thatch look as though they are to be thwarted by a district council, do not needlessly lose heart. The officers dealing with appeals at the Department of the Environment are, fortunately, not unreasonable people, and as long as your case is sound and well presented, you should stand a good chance of succeeding. If in doubt, use the services of a planning consultant experienced with thatch.

Air bricks in roof cavities

The Building Regulations now require the use of air bricks in the roof void of newly-built houses to allow a flow of air to protect against rot in the timbers. This is due to the conventionally-roofed house being insulated at bedroom ceiling joist height and therefore a change of temperature occurs between bedrooms and loft. Thatch, however, insulates at roof level and air bricks are therefore unnecessary as the problem of rot is avoided.

So does the entire empty loft space therefore require heating? The answer with a conventional thatched roof is yes. There is no harm in conforming to the regulations for tiled or slated roofs by insulating at ceiling joist level and installing air bricks, but the thatch is then little more than a cosmetic addition as its insulative qualities are wasted.

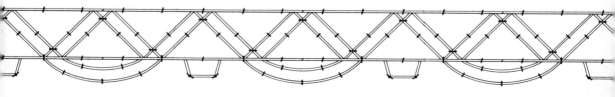

7
Learning
the Art of Thatching

Even experienced thatchers continue to learn more about their craft throughout their working lives, but given reasonable intelligence, stamina and a good eye, a keen trainee can be taught to thatch to a high standard within a relatively short time.

The conventional apprenticeship was designed for school leavers and normally lasted five years. It was the teaching of a craft by a master man who still had to earn a living whilst slowly bringing on a young person who perhaps was not fitted either physically or mentally at 16 years of age for the rigours of a complete day on and off a roof. This type of training was not without value but it was slow, repetitive and frequently boring. The apprentice was in truth little more than a low-paid labourer for a substantial part of the training period.

Attitudes have changed over the last forty years and, with a few exceptions, it has been accepted that the old form of apprenticeship is no longer reasonable or practical in modern competitive society. The alternative is to select an adult who has already had work experience, and who understands both the physical and mental pressures of a demanding job, and put him through a structured, intensive training course for six months. During that period he will acquire proficiency in probably 80 per cent of everything he needs to know about thatching, and over the following few years he should be able to draw on the expert knowledge of his teacher as and when necessary. This type of training programme has already produced men who are above the national average in ability, and a handful who are in the top 5 to 10 per cent of all thatchers. The old, proven system, which in some form will always continue, must not be decried, but nor must it be assumed that thatching is so complex and mysterious that it cannot be learnt quickly.

Plate 111 Getting the weatherlap right. An apprentice at the beginning of his course working on a mock-up roof under cover

Plate 112 Within a few days pupils can begin to learn more complicated techniques, such as cutting the eaves

113▶

114▶

Plate 113 Their first ridge and patterning have been attempted; now work progresses to the gables
Plate 114 A difficult cheek shape competently executed on the mock-up roof
Plate 115 Work completed to a very high standard by novice thatchers; all their mistakes have been made on the practice roof
Plate 116 Intricate shapes can be tackled within a few months, under constant guidance and supervision

▲115

▼116

Plate 117 *In less than a year from starting the structured course, trainees are turning out this work*

Plate 118 *Thatched (with minimal supervision) by men who had started their training only eighteen months previously*

The following would be a fairly typical six-month course for trainee thatchers:

Day 1. The first lessons are in the workshops, where the pupils are taught to make the simple wooden tools they will need to repair and remake many times over the next few years.

Day 2. The trainees will be handling materials, butting and clipping combed wheat reed bundles, twisting spars and, before the day is out, tying eaves wads on to mock-up roofs and laying the brow and subsequent courses.

Day 3. This will be spent tying eaves wads and laying courses of combed wheat reed on a mock-up roof under cover. All the mistakes in the world can happen here, and better that they do — once corrected they will not be repeated on a real roof. By the end of the first week the trainees will be laying flat straight work on the mock up.

In the following week they will put all they have learned into practice up on a real roof, but under supervision. Once they have mastered these techniques, they go back to the mock up where they will learn the method of laying a valley. Again they return to the roof to put it into practice (see page 152).

Each facet of the roof will be covered in this way using more than one material. On rainy days the trainees are taken through the skills of measuring and estimating, book keeping and VAT or splitting hazel and making spars.

With the intensity of teaching it is essential that a trainee is not only physically and mentally capable of learning and doing the job properly, but also that he really *wants* to learn.

Glossary
of Technical Terms

Plate 119
Backfill

Apron See **Skirts**.

Backfill
A thin layer of thatch laid on top of battens to allow courses of thatch to slide up the roof frame without catching on the timbers. (Only on new roofs.)

Barge
The finished edge of thatch overhanging the gable. Also known as: brow; flue; gable.

Base coat
Plate 120 Barge Original layer of thatch.

Bat See **Leggett**.
Bed A prepared heap of wetted long straw from which a yealm is drawn.
Beetle See **Leggett**.

Plate 121
Base coat
Plate 122 Bed

Plate 123
Biddle

Biddle
Small two- or three-runged ladder with curved prongs for inserting into thatch and kneeling on.

Bottles
Tightly tied individual bundles of thatch used to form the eaves. Also known as eaves bundles or wads.

Brotches (or Broaches)
See **Spars**.

Brow   See **Barge**.

Brow course
First course up from the eaves bottles.

Plate 124
Bottles

136

Plate 125
Brow course

Capping   See **Ridge**.

Coat   Complete covering of thatch.

Coating   One new complete layer of thatch fitted to an existing older coat.

Course   Strip of thatch laid horizontally along the roof.

Crooks   Steel nails varying in length from 100 to 355mm (4–14in) used for securing reed. Alternative names: hooks; spikes.

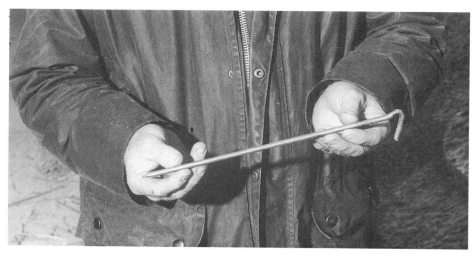

Plate 126 Crook

137

Plate 127
Cross spars **Cross spars** Strips of split hazel or willow used for decorating and securing the ridge.

Devon reed Combed wheat reed.

Dolly See **Ridge roll**.

Dresser See **Leggett**.

Dutchman A rounded wooden tool used for forming valleys in thatch in a similar way to a leggett.

Plate 128
Dutchman

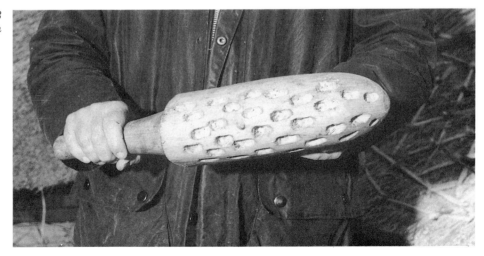

Plate 129
Eaves hook

Eaves bundles   See **Bottles**.
Eaves hook (or Eaves knife)   Hook for cutting the eaves.
Eaves wads   See **Bottles**.
Fathom   Six bundles of Norfolk reed laid together, with a circumference of 1.8m (6ft) measured 30cm (12in) from the butts.
Flashing   Lead or cement strip fitted at the junction of a chimney, wall or window to make it watertight.
Flue   See **Barge**.
Gable   See **Barge**.
Gads   See **Osier**.
Hooks   See **Crooks**.
Hovers knife   Long-bladed and long-handled knife used for cutting gables/barges in long straw.

Plate 130
Hovers knife

Plate 131
Leggett

Ledgers   See **Liggers**; **Sways**.

Leggett   Wooden tool, shaped like a bat with a grooved surface, used to dress or drive water reed and combed wheat reed in place. Alternative names: bat; beetle, dresser.

Liggers   Hazel or willow saplings 1.5m (5ft) long, pegged down by spars, used for securing and decorating thatch. Also known as: ledgers; rods; runners; sways.

Nails   See **Crooks**.

Needle   Metal or wooden tool resembling a large flat-sided sewing needle which is threaded with twine at the pointed end for fixing thatch to the battens.

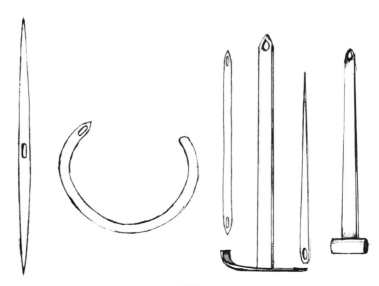

140

Plate 132
Pinnacle

Nitch   A bundle of combed wheat reed.
Osier   Willow for splitting into spars or liggers. Also known as a gad.
Pattern spars   See **Cross spars**.
Peak   See **Pinnacle**.
Pinnacle   Raised end of ridge surmounting gable or top point or hip. Also known as the peak.
Ridge   The apex of the roof which completes the thatch. Also known as the capping or roving.

Plate 133
Ridge

Plate 134
Side pin

Plate 135
Side rake

142

Ridge roll   Bundle of tightly-tied reed or straw, 100–200mm (4–8in) in diameter and of any suitable length, used for building up the ridge prior to capping. Also known as a dolly.

Rods   See **Liggers**; **Sways**.

Roving   See **Ridge**.

Runners   See **Liggers**.

Saddle   The material (sedge, rye or wheat straw) laid over the ridge and secured with liggers and spars.

Shearing hook   Hook for shearing surface of thatch to its final finish.

Side pin   Large, flat-sided metal or wooden pin used to temporarily hold course ends upright.

Side rake   Tool resembling a comb used to tidy the surface of a long straw coat.

Skirts   (see pp 144–5)

Spar hook   A small billhook used for cutting, splitting and sharpening hazel or willow spars.

Spar   Split hazel or willow saplings about 60cm (24in) long, triangular (usually) in section, bent through 180 degrees and used for securing new thatch to old or securing liggers whilst ridging. Alternative terms: broaches; brotches; spicks, spitts; sprays; staples.

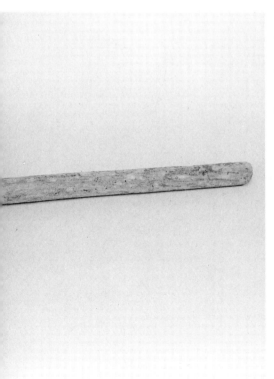

Plate 136 Spars

143

Skirts The layer of thatch under chimneys or windows, or completing a block-cut ridge, which is fixed on the surface with spars and liggers. Also known as the apron.

Plate 137 Skirts

Spicks   See **Spars**.

Spikes   See **Crooks**.

Spitts   See **Spars**.

Sprays   See **Spars**.

Staples   See **Spars**.

Straw bond   Length of straw twisted horizontally across the course and sparred down to fasten the thatch.

Straw rope   A continuous length of rope made from twisted straw, used for spar fixing.

Stulch   The strip of thatch, twice the width of a ladder, laid from eaves to ridge as work proceeds.

Sways

Long rods or liggers made of hazel, willow or steel, used for securing the layers (courses) of water reed. They are laid at right angles to the direction of the reed and tied with tarred cord or fixed by iron hooks to the rafters.

Tarred twine

Strong cord treated with Stockholm tar, used for stitching or tying thatch to battens and rafters.

Thatchboard See **Flaking**.
Thatch hooks See **Crooks**.
Thatch nails See **Crooks**.

Yealm

A prepared layer of wet straw or sedge, approximately 350–450mm (14–18in) wide and 100mm (4in) thick used for either coat work or ridge saddles in long straw, combed wheat reed or sedge — but not water reed.

Yealm holder

Hazel fork in which yealms are carried up to the roof.

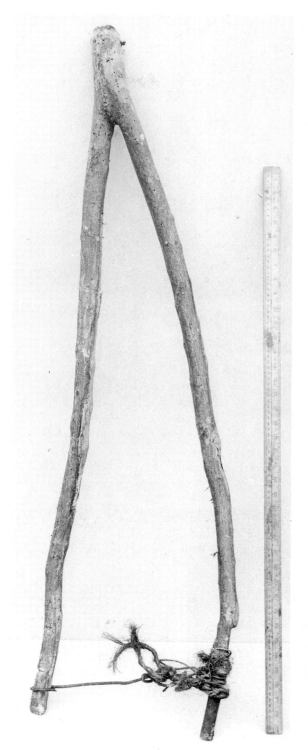

Plate 140 Yealm holder

147

Appendix:
How to Find a Thatcher

How does one find a thatcher? And is it possible to tell if one is getting a skilled, honest, businesslike craftsman? There are no short answers. It is possible that a houseowner is about to spend several thousand pounds on a thatch, so it is only reasonable that some time is spent on researching the quality of the thatcher undertaking the work.

There are trade associations, local county associations, a National Society and a guild of master craftsmen, but membership of these associations is not in itself a guarantee of a quality thatcher. There are just as many highly skilled and honest thatchers outside the trade associations as within, and frequently they can offer more competitive prices. Yellow Pages is a reasonable starting point if you do not have any personal recommendations to follow up. Contact three or four thatchers and ask them to advise you on what needs to be done to your roof, at what price and when. There are horses for courses in thatching and it is frequently difficult to make a fair comparison; none the less you can ask each of them for a detailed specification (see below).

In addition, ask the thatchers about any work they have completed recently, and visit the properties. People who live in thatched houses generally love to talk about them so don't hesitate to knock on the door and introduce yourself. It will not take many visits before you begin to see the difference between good, fair and bad thatching and the price relationship between the qualities of thatch. Did the thatcher start the work when he said he would? Did he take a reasonable time to complete it? Did he stick to his price, or did he increase it at the last minute? Were his customers satisfied with him? Quality alone is probably not enough — any thatcher can turn out 'Rolls-Royce' work if he has taken two years over the job and it is possibly better to have more modest work done in one month at a reasonable price.

No one should want to standardise a craft industry like thatching; the result would surely be to bring about its decline.

One only has to look at the Francis Frith Photographic Collection (a collection of Victorian black and white photographs recording British life) to note that there was considerably more thatching 100 years ago and that much of it would today be labelled as the work of 'cowboys', which, of course, it was not. The attainment of perfection is a just and worthy cause, but not if the price to pay for it is the extinction of the industry. Long may there be variation, long may the public be free to choose their own standards and long may the farmer keep his barn thatched (even though corrugated iron is cheaper).

SPECIFICATIONS

The sample specification given below is only a guide but will provide a basis for the comparison of costs and standards of work:

1 Prepare old coat: ie strip existing roof to a firm foundation/strip eaves and barges (gables)/remove wire mesh.
2 Material: long straw/combed wheat reed (Devon reed)/water reed (Norfolk type).
3 Sew in new eaves and gables.
4 Lay full coat approximately $x$mm thick [usually 200–375mm (8–15in)].
5 Lay block-cut patterned ridge/flush ridge/block-cut butt-up ridge/butt-up flush ridge/Devon twist ridge.
6 Fix wire mesh (20 or 22 gauge) to all slopes/ridge only.
7 Clear up site and dispose of all waste.
8 Price.
9 Date for commencement.
10 Estimated date of completion.

Additional costs will occasionally have to be taken into consideration for each foot run of hips, valleys and windows; it is very unlikely that there will be any additional cost for eaves and barges. Similarly the thatcher will quote per foot for the ridging cost. Should the roof require scaffolding — frequently a very expensive item — this will also be added to the contract price.

Do your homework and expect a quality commensurate with price. There are a few thatchers left who are not registered for VAT and the only way that this is legally possible is for the client to buy the materials and the thatcher to charge for labour only — perfectly acceptable and a possible way of saving costs.

Useful Addresses

The Museum of English Rural Life
Reading University

Thatching Advisory Service Ltd
Rose Tree Farm
29 Nine Mile Ride
Finchampstead
Berks, RG11 4QD

The Guild of Master Craftsmen
166 High Street
Lewes
East Sussex, BN7 1YE

The Council for Small Industries in
 Rural Areas
Salisbury
Wilts

The National Society of Master
 Thatchers
38 Bradford Road
Toddington
Beds

Town Planning Consultancy
89 Southwark Street
London
SE1 0HX

*What a novice can achieve after a few days'
instruction (*The Museum of English Rural
Life, Reading University)

Further Reading

Fearn, Jaqueline, *Thatch and Thatching*, Shire Publications (1976)
Stowe, E. J., *Thatching of Rick and Barn*, Landsmans Library (1954)
Council for Small Industries in Rural Areas, *The Thatcher's Craft*
Norfolk Reed Growers' Association, *The Reed*
Edlin, Herbert L., *Woodland Crafts in Britain*, David & Charles (1973).
   Useful information on hazel coppicing

Acknowledgements

I would like to acknowledge the help given to me by the following people: Art Barnes, Louis Turpin, Ethan Danielson, Geoff and Scott Sharp, Valerie Jackson, Russell Cooper ARICS, H. F. Wooner BA MRTPI, the Thatchers from Master Thatchers Ltd and all the staff at the Thatching Advisory Service Ltd.

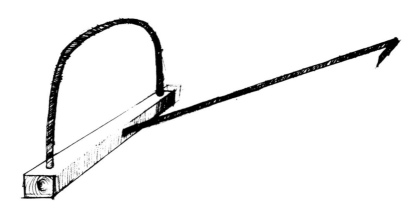

Index